Pocket Pal®

A Graphic Arts Production Handbook

Eleventh Edition

INTERNATIONAL PAPER COMPANY

First Edition - 1934
Second Edition - September 1938
Third Edition - October 1954
Fourth Edition - November 1955
Fifth Edition - October 1957
Sixth Edition - April 1960
Seventh Edition - June 1963
Eighth Edition - November 1964
Ninth Edition - February 1966
Tenth Edition - May 1970
Tenth Edition, Rev. - January 1973
Eleventh Edition - December 1974
   Second Printing - January 1976
   Third Printing - March 1978

Price: $2.25

foreword

Ever since its debut in 1934, the Pocket Pal has served as an excellent introduction to the graphic arts for many artists, designers, advertisers, buyers of printing and students. Acclaimed by most authorities as the best publication of its type, International Paper Company has continually strived to improve its content and keep it current.

At the time of Pocket Pal's first edition, printing was predominantly letterpress, and the other processes, lithography, gravure, and screen printing, were upstarts used mainly for special purposes. In the past forty years, the situation has changed dramatically. Now the term "Printing" no longer refers solely to letterpress but encompasses all the graphic arts processes. Letterpress has gradually given way to lithography in commercial, book, newspaper and magazine printing, while gravure continues to make appreciable gains in catalog, publishing, packaging and other specialty areas.

In the 10th edition, the format of the Pocket Pal was changed to present each of the printing processes in its proper perspective. This 11th edition incorporates the many changes and developments that have occurred in the past few years. It also assesses the effect of these changes on the future of the printing industry.

Appreciation is expressed for the help of Frank J. Romano in revising the section on Photographic Typesetting and Wayne Gilgore for sections on Copiers and Reprography.

Michael H. Bruno
Corporate Consultant, Graphic Arts
International Paper Company

contents

history

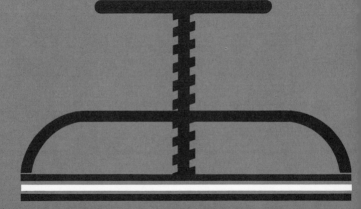

THE EVOLUTION OF PRINTING

Printing is something which can be seen, perceived with our eyes and reproduced in quantity. Regardless of the many possible differences, all printed products have one thing in common: *the result is always a quantity of the same visible image.*

Man's earliest known attempt at a visual record of his life and times dates back 30,000 years. These were wall drawings called pictographs, superseded by the more complex ideographs. They in turn were succeeded by the Persians' cuneiforms, and then by hieroglyphics, perfected by the Egyptians around 2500 B.C. Ten centuries later the Phoenicians used the first formal alphabet. But these are art forms and not printing as it is usually defined.

Evidence of the first example of printing from movable type was discovered in 1908 by an Italian archaeologist on the island of Crete. He found a clay disc in the ruins of the palace of Phaistos in a stratification dated about 1500 B.C.

Printing from movable type appeared in China and Korea in the 11th century. In 1041, a Chinese, Pi-Sheng, developed type characters from hardened clay. They were not wholly successful. Type cast from metal in Korea was widely used in China and Japan, and by the middle 1200s type characters were being cast in bronze. The oldest text known was printed from such type in Korea in 1397 A.D.

Half a century later in 1440, probably unaware of the crude type developed in the Orient, Johann Gutenberg brought the West up to date with his invention of movable type. Until Gutenberg's system of separate characters for printing on a press with ink on paper, all books were laboriously hand written by scribes. Little wonder that historians credit his invention as the beginning of printing, coinciding with the end of the Middle Ages and the beginning of Modern History.

Paper and printing ink were not new when Gutenberg's type appeared. The use of parchment was introduced for writing by Eumenes, king of Pergamus, in 170 B.C. Two hundred years later, Wang Ch'ung, a Chinese philosopher, used bamboo as a writing surface. Another Chinese, Ts'ai Lun, is credited with the invention of paper in 105 A.D. By the time Gutenberg was born, papermaking was a well-developed industry throughout the Western hemisphere with paper mills existing in Spain, France, Italy and Germany.

In making ink for printing, the Chinese also led the world in discovery. Wei Tang perfected an ink for block printing using lampblack in 400 A.D. Viscous or tacky inks, essential to printing, were already in use in Germany for block printing and for stamping titles on manuscript bookbindings by Gutenberg's time.

To Gutenberg we must attribute the envisionment of commercial and cultural possibilities of printing as a process of graphic reproduction. To the cumulative effect of inventions of many minds in a growing civilization, we must attribute the evolution of printing as a graphic art.

TYPE BEGINNINGS

Our common type faces are either imitations of early hand-written letters or represent a modification of early type faces which, in turn, were modeled after the lettering in manuscript books.

The standard *roman* lower-case letters and capitals assumed their present form about 1470 in a face cut by Nicolas Jenson. While Jenson, a Frenchman, learned printing in Germany, he did his first printing in Venice, Italy. The letters inscribed in manuscript books by Venetian monks were Jenson's models. His types served as a pattern for later faces. Jenson was not the first to use roman letters, but he must receive credit for developing a beautiful face upon which no later designer has been able to improve significantly. Type faces similar to Jenson are often called Venetian types.

The first books in Europe were printed in black-letter or *gothic* type. They were designed to imitate the style of letter used by religious scribes living in the vicinity of Mainz, Germany, where Gutenberg began his printing activities. John Fust and Peter Schoeffer, who entered the printing field through business relations with Gutenberg, continued to use the gothic letter form. Thus, the gothic letter became firmly established in Northern Europe.

To avoid confusion, it must be pointed out that the term "gothic," as used by some modern typefounders to designate

SETTING TYPE BY HAND   EARLY TYPE FACES

Roman Type

a

Gothic Type

𝖆

sans serif types, has no relation to gothic as a description of early type faces. Gothic, as a term applied to architecture and other forms of art, designates the style characteristic of Northern and Western Europe from the twelfth to sixteenth century. It is in this sense that gothic is also applied to letter forms.

ROMAN LETTER DEVELOPMENT

The manuscript hand of the Venetian scribes, which Nicolas Jenson followed as his model, developed apart from gothic lettering. It had evolved from roman capital letters. In formal writing and inscriptions the early Romans used square capitals, with slight modifications, in the form of our upper-case alphabet. For correspondence and documents not requiring formal writing, large cursive or running capitals were used.

Many national styles in writing developed as learning was carried from Rome throughout the rest of the known world. The influence of the roman characters might have been lost, however, had not Emperor Charlemagne taken an interest in the revival and spread of ancient learning. Charlemagne encouraged the establishment of a school at Tours by an English scholar named Alcuin. The calligraphy of this school became the model for the rest of Europe.

By the tenth century the use of letter forms from which we derive our lower case was quite universal. However, these letters did not assume the fixed form with which we are familiar until they were cast in types by Jenson.

ITALICS AND DISPLAY TYPES

Practically all roman type faces in common use today have accompanying *italics*. This was not true of early roman faces. Jenson, for example, did not produce *cursive* type; italics were a separate development.

Italics were first used to print small, compact books. Early books were large and cumbersome, for gothic type used in these books was large. When roman type came into use, it was cast smaller than gothic, and letters and lines were fitted more closely. But even this economy in page size did not satisfy Aldus Manutius, a Venetian printer around the turn of the fifteenth century. Sensing a growing trend for cheaper books, he tried to meet the demand by cutting a font of type to imitate the informal handwriting of his time. Aldus called this type *Chancery;* his Italian contemporaries called it *Aldine;* but in the rest of Europe, the face was called *italic.* This latter designation has continued in use to the present time.

Display types of today are difficult to trace historically. All were derived from hand-drawn letters. They may have been specifically drawn as a type-design or developed from a letter drawn for another purpose.

EARLY PRINTING IN ENGLAND

We are interested in early printing in England because it was through England that printing came to the American colonies. Printing was introduced in England about 1476 by William Caxton, who brought equipment from the Netherlands to establish a press at Westminster. Among the books issued from Caxton's press were Chaucer's *The Canterbury Tales, Fables of Aesop,* and many other popular works.

The predecessor of the modern Oxford University Press was established in 1585. Since that date the press has operated continuously, probably the longest period of any printing establishment in history.

Richard Pynson, who printed in England during the latter part of the fifteenth and early sixteenth centuries, is believed to have been the first to introduce roman types in England. John Day, who began printing on his own account in 1546, was the first English designer of a roman type face.

TWO FAMOUS ENGLISH TYPE DESIGNERS

William Caslon, born in 1692 in Worcestershire, was destined to change the appearance of English printing through the design and casting of a new type face. Not only is Caslon type still used, but his style of printing is still consciously or unconsciously followed by many contemporary typographers. An axiom of printers with a type problem is, "When in doubt, use Caslon!"

Although Caslon's letters are not perfect in themselves, a page of Caslon type produces a simple, pleasing and balanced effect.

The English printer and typographer, John Baskerville, born in 1706, is regarded by some students of the history of printing as the father of fine printing in England. Baskerville, after having accumulated a fair-sized fortune in other fields, established a paper mill, printing office and type foundry at Birmingham in 1750.

Baskerville spent several years experimenting with designs for type. He also tried to improve the surface of sheets of paper by pressing them between hot plates after printing, and he mixed special inks which were used in producing his first book.

Consequently, when he offered his first printed works to the public around 1757, they gained wide acclaim.

The types designed by Baskerville are usually considered to represent a half-way step between the *old-style* roman letter which Caslon so clearly exemplified and the *modern* style of roman letter which is best illustrated by the face developed by the Italian printer, Bodoni.

England's contribution to the development of printing was not as great as that of countries in Continental Europe. However, it was through English printers that the early traditions of printing in America were established.

EARLY PRINTING IN AMERICA

Printing was used to promote colonization of the New World. There is on file in the New York Public Library a copy of such a promotion piece dated 1609. It is entitled, "Offering Most Excellent Fruites by Planting in Virginia." One historian, observing the fact that 750 of the first 900 settlers in the Virginia Colonies died during the first winter, marvels at the force of the printed word. It not only induced new settlers to come to the New World, but also influenced the 150 survivors to remain.

The extent to which printing was used in promoting the New England Colonies is not known. But it is known that a printing press made its appearance in Massachusetts soon after the first settlers established themselves. It is conceivable that the press and printing materials, brought from England in 1638, were used to produce religious and political tracts to be circulated in the mother country. This belief is fortified by the fact that the first piece printed on the new press was *The Freeman's Oath.*

Conditions changed in England, and the press which might have been intended as a propaganda machine was turned to service for the Colonists. The *Bay Psalm Book,* eleven copies of which are still in existence, was produced in 1640. It was printed on an early colonial press procured in England by Reverend Jose Glover. The Reverend Glover died on the voyage to America, but his wife assumed responsibility for setting up the press in Cambridge. Stephen Daye, who had been indentured by the Reverend Glover to operate the press, was placed in charge by Mistress Glover and, with his son, Matthew, continued its operation until 1647.

In the meantime, Glover's widow was married again, this time to President Dunster of Harvard College. Upon her death the press was moved to Harvard and used in close association with the college. In a sense, this represents the beginning of

Harvard University Press, the oldest continuously operated printing activity in America.

Printing did not make headway in the southern colonies to the extent that it did in the Massachusetts Colony. A printing venture undertaken by William Nuthead in Jamestown, in 1682, was suppressed by the King's governor. Three years later William Bradford began printing in Philadelphia, but after several unpleasant conflicts with colonial officials he was forced to abandon his work. Subsequently, he was permitted to move to New York where he again became engaged in printing.

By 1700 there were at least a dozen printers in Boston. By 1763 there was a press in operation in Georgia, the last of the thirteen colonies to be settled. Printing came to Kentucky, Tennessee, Ohio and Michigan in the 1780's and 1790's. In 1808 printing had moved west of the Mississippi to St. Louis. Thus, as migration continued west, printing followed.

TWO PRINTER PATRIOTS

Benjamin Franklin, believed by some to have been the most important American citizen of his time, was born in Boston in 1706. As a boy he learned printing in the shop of his brother. In 1723 he quarrelled with his brother and went to New York. Unable to find work, he continued on to Philadelphia where he worked for a French printer named Keimer.

At the suggestion of the governor of Pennsylvania, Sir William Keith, young Franklin went to England to buy a printing outfit. Money which he had been promised was not forthcoming, so for two years he worked in famous English printing plants, including that of William Watts. In 1726 he returned to Philadelphia. By 1732 he had his own printing office and became the publisher of the *Pennsylvania Gazette.* Among the publications Franklin printed, *Poor Richard's Almanack* became the most famous.

Throughout his life, Franklin was active in promoting printing. Although he disposed of his business in Philadelphia in 1748 to devote his time to literary, journalistic and civic activities, he assisted in the establishment and promotion of forty or more printing plants in the Colonies. Franklin's high regard for his craft is revealed by the words with which he began his will: "I, Benjamin Franklin, Printer . . . "

Franklin is not the only printer of the Revolutionary Period who is celebrated as a great patriot. There are several; outstanding among them is Isaiah Thomas. Thomas, born in Massachusetts in 1744, was actively engaged in printing early in his life. In 1770 he began publication of the *Massachusetts Spy,* a newspaper in which he supported the cause of the patriots. He served during the Revolutionary War as printer for the Massachusetts House of Assembly. Following the war, he re-established his business which had been destroyed. As a printer he prospered and became the leading publisher of books in the period following the Revolution. In 1810 he published a two-volume *History of Printing in America* which, even today, remains the best source on colonial printing.

TYPE AND TYPECASTING MACHINES

For more than four hundred years after the invention of printing, all type was set by hand. In the nineteenth century, men began to consider the possibility of creating typesetting machines. Numerous machines intended to replace hand composition were invented. The first of these was designed by an Englishman, Dr. William Church, in 1822; others soon followed. While

CHURCH'S TYPESETTING MACHINE

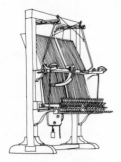

many of the first typesetting machines functioned satisfactorily, none were sufficiently practical for commercial operation until the invention of the linotype by Ottmar Mergenthaler in 1886.

Of the various metal composing machines developed, only two kinds are still in use. These are machines such as the Linotype, Intertype, and Ludlow which cast *slugs* (one-piece fully spaced lines); and the Monotype which casts *individual pieces of type* in justified lines.

The Monotype was invented in 1887 by Tolbert Lanston of Washington, D.C. The Ludlow Typograph was suggested by Washington I. Ludlow in 1906 and later perfected by William A. Reade. Intertype, a later development in 1911, utilizes the Mergenthaler principle. The most recent development in machine composition is photographic typesetting.

PLATEMAKING BEFORE THE 20TH CENTURY

The first illustrations in books were made from woodcuts. They were tooled out of wood blocks by hand, leaving raised surfaces. The earliest known book using woodcuts was printed by Albrecht Pfister in Bamberg about 1460.

Books printed between 1570 and 1770 were usually illustrated by copperplate engravings, resulting in a decline in the making of woodcuts. In 1770, however, a revival was started by Thomas Bewick of England who developed the technique of using a special engraving tool for cutting *across* the grain, instead of *with* the grain. Today, woodcuts are used only to give an "artistic touch" to certain types of printed pieces.

Engraved copper intaglio plates, the forerunner of steel engravings and gravure, were first used in France and Italy around 1476. Copper engraving offered competition to woodcuts in England about 1545, and in France about 1569. Copperplate work has continued to be practiced through the years and is still used for invitations and announcements.

The invention of photoengraving parallels the discovery and development of photographic methods. In 1824 Joseph Niepce, the partner of Louis Daguerre, made the first metal engraving by photography. All later production of etched printing plates depended upon this discovery. In 1839 Ponton of Edinburgh developed the sensitizing method later used in photoengraving.

The screen principle was discovered by an Englishman, William Talbot, in 1852. Using the same methods as Niepce, he produced the first halftone photoengraving by laying a screen of fine gauze between the coated metal and negative of the original picture. This created the "dot pattern" as it is known today.

Photoengraving developed rapidly in America, and by 1871 it was commercially practicable for letterpress printing. By 1880 photoengraved prints were replacing woodcuts as illustrations in books and magazines. In that year, Stephen Horgan made the first halftone photoengraving for printing. It utilized a coarse screen and was printed by lithography in *The Daily Graphic* of New York, the first picture newspaper.

The first commercial halftone screen was produced in 1883 by Max and Louis Levy of Philadelphia. Two years later Frederick Ives improved on their technique by developing the earliest version of the crossline screen that is used in photoengraving today. Although the first halftones were black and white, the application of halftones to color process printing was not long in developing. Color process work was successfully printed in 1893, and today is one of the most widely used methods of graphic reproduction.

The advancement of photoengraving, and photomechanics in general, was dependent on F. Scott Archer's invention in 1851 of the wet collodion process for photography. This process flourished for many years, even after photographic dry plates became available in 1879 and film in 1888.

DEVELOPMENT OF THE PRINTING PRESS

In hand composition there is much in common between printing today and printing as it was practiced by the followers of Gutenberg. The general appearance of type, its casting, and the procedures used in putting it together to form words, lines and pages have not radically changed.

In transferring the impression to paper by the use of printing presses, however, radical changes have occurred. The crude wooden hand presses of the early printers, capable of turning out 300 to 500 sheets in a day, have been replaced with power driven machines which produce the same number of impressions in a few minutes (in newspaper printing, a few seconds).

Benjamin Franklin worked on a wooden-frame press in the printing office of William Watts in London. This press used a torsion screw for making the impression and was provided with

STEPHEN DAYE PRESS

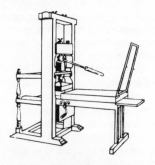

a clever mechanical arrangement devised to provide the proper pressure on the form. This was an improvement over the Stephen Daye press, which was brought to Cambridge from London in 1638. Further changes in press construction came about slowly until the first all-metal press was built by the Earl of Stanhope early in the nineteenth century. This press still used a screw device, but less exertion was required to force the impression on the sheet. Application of the principle of the lever to the iron press resulted in several presses which came into common use. Among these were the Columbian Press, built by George Clymer of New York; the Albion Press, invented by R. W. Cope of London; and the Washington Press, perfected by Samuel Rust. The Washington Press became popular in the United States, and by 1900 over 6,000 had been sold. The Albion Press was equally popular in England.

The idea of the printing press, as conceived by Gutenberg, reached its highest development in the Washington and Albion Presses. The modern job press and the cylinder press are distinctly different machines. However, the first power press did have some of the features of the hand presses. The Adams Press, patented by Isaac Adams in 1830, raised and lowered the form by means of a steam-powered cam, which operated a toggle joint. In appearance, the Adams Press has been described as "an old-fashioned hand press turned upside down."

The modern job, or platen, press is the direct descendant of a machine perfected in 1858 by George P. Gordon of New York. In this machine the platen and form are turned on edge. Of the models manufactured today, some employ a rigid bed, with the platen drawn up against the form. In others, both the platen and bed move with a sort of clamshell action.

The modern cylinder press was first conceived by William Nicholson of London who secured patents in 1790 but was unable to perfect a working model. The first steam-powered cylinder press was built in London under the supervision of a German named Frederick König, who seemed to have known something of Nicholson's ideas. It was used for printing *The London Times* in 1814 and was capable of producing 1,100 sheets per hour. A rotating cylinder was used to press the paper against a flat type bed.

Most modern flat-bed cylinder presses trace back to König's first cylinder machine. Shortly after König's press was placed in operation in 1814, D. Napier, an Englishman, invented a press using grippers for picking up the sheet from the paper table and holding it while the sheet received the impression.

Numerous other improvements have been added throughout the years, and while most present-day cylinder presses produce up to 5,000 impressions per hour, they are gradually becoming obsolete. No flat-bed cylinder presses, except the vertical press, are produced in the U.S. anymore.

In the United States, Richard Hoe perfected the first rotary press in 1847, with the type actually carried on the cylinder. Early models produced 2,000 impressions per hour per cylinder.

HOE'S TEN-CYLINDER PRESS

The first web press was developed by an American, William Bullock, in 1856. A similar press was patented ten years later in London. These early presses delivered 15,000 signatures per hour printed both sides. A device for folding the papers as they came from the press was added in 1875.

Since that time newspaper presses have been developed to a high state of efficiency. The Wood-Hoe Colormatic press prints 128 pages from eight rolls of paper. It slits, folds and collects 8-page signatures to make four 32-page sections at the rate of 80,000 per hour. By duplicating plates and units, newspapers can be delivered at the rate of 160,000 per hour.

DISCOVERY OF LITHOGRAPHY

The basic principle of lithography, "writing on stone", was discovered by Alois Senefelder of Munich around 1798. Working on a highly porous stone, he sketched his design with a greasy substance which was absorbed by the stone. He then wetted the entire surface with a mixture of gum arabic and water. Only the blank areas absorbed the solution; the design area repelled it. Rolling on an ink made of soap, wax, oil and lampblack, this substance, being greasy, coated the design but did not spread over the moist blank area. A clean impression of the design was then made when a sheet of paper was pressed against the surface of the stone.

Artists soon used this new process to make reproductions of the works of old masters and, in time, recognized it as a valuable medium for their own original works. It received its biggest boost towards recognition when Currier and Ives popularized lithography in the middle of the 19th century. This new recogni-

SENEFELDER'S PRESS

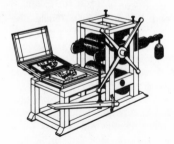

tion and popularity encouraged printers to find more practical and faster methods using the principle of lithography.

The first American steam press for lithography was designed by R. Hoe of New York about 1868. Stones transferred the image; the "steam" operated an engine that drove the press, just as an electric motor does now.

In 1906 the first "offset" press as we know it today began rolling out printed sheets in Nutley, New Jersey, an invention of Ira A. Rubel, a paper manufacturer. Actually the discovery was an accident. An impression was unintentionally printed from a press cylinder directly onto the rubber blanket of the impression cylinder. Immediately afterwards, when a sheet of paper was run through the press, a sharp image was printed on it from the impression which had been "offset" on the rubber blanket. A. F. Harris had noticed a similar effect, and he too developed an offset press for the Harris Automatic Press Company of Niles, Ohio, in the same year, 1906.

HISTORY OF PRINTING PAPERS

Papermaking was invented in China nearly 2000 years ago. By 1200 A.D. paper was being made in Spain, and 200 years later the art was well established throughout Europe. The first paper mill in England was built in 1494. In the American colonies paper was first manufactured commercially in 1690, in a mill near Philadelphia owned by William Rittenhouse. Paper originally was made for uses other than printing; but, with the invention of the printing press, changes in the products of paper mills and in the methods of manufacturing began to be made.

Ancient papers were made almost entirely from rags and were produced with crude hand-operated devices. Most papers currently used in printing are manufactured from wood pulp. Only writing and ledger papers are made from rags to any great extent, and even these contain a percentage of wood pulp.

The machine for producing a continuous web of paper was invented by a Frenchman, Louis Robert, in 1798. His invention was financed and developed by an English family, the Fourdriniers and even today, a papermaking machine is referred to as a "Fourdrinier."

The manufacturing of paper from groundwood pulp was introduced to the world in 1840. Production of cellulose, or wood fibre, by chemical methods, using caustic soda, was perfected in 1854. The use of bisulphite of lime, in the chemical production of pulp, came into use about 1866. Both mechanical (groundwood) and chemical pulps are now widely used.

HISTORY OF PRINTING INKS

No history of printing would be complete without some mention of the history of inkmaking. As stated at the start of this section, ink was already in use for printing from wood blocks at the time Gutenberg developed his movable type system. Actually, the origin of printing ink is shrouded in mystery. It developed from writing ink which was used by the Egyptians and Chinese as early as 2600 B.C. These early inks consisted of lampblack or soot mixed with animal glue or vegetable oils. Inkmaking became a highly developed art among the Chinese as they introduced earth colors and printed from hand cut blocks in the 11th century – 400 years before Gutenberg.

In the early days the printer made his own inks using lampblack and boiled linseed oil which he cooked according to his own "secret" formula. Inkmaking developed on a commercial scale in the 16th and 17th centuries. The first ink factory was established in America in 1742. Little color was used until the discovery of coal tar dyes in the middle of the nineteenth century. Now inkmaking has been highly refined with special inks for each process and purpose, and represents a half-billion dollar industry in the U.S. alone.

While Gutenberg did well to produce a single one-color impression in three minutes, today's great rotary presses easily print multi-color on both sides of a continuous roll of paper, at the rate of over 2,000 feet per minute. Not only have presses been speeded up, but films, plates, papers, inks and all other materials have been improved, so that printing is now a mature combination of processes and techniques which make up the subject matter for the remainder of the *Pocket Pal.*

printing today and tomorrow

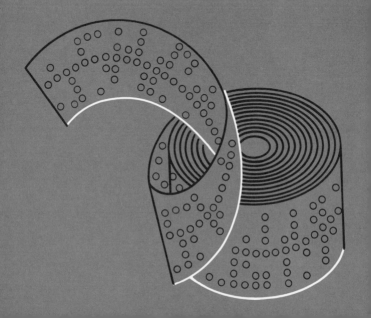

Printing and publishing is big business. It represents about 3% of the gross national product. Among all U.S. manufacturing industries in the most recent figures available, it ranked first in the total number of establishments—38,000—with 80% having less than 20 employees, second in average hourly gross earnings per production worker, seventh in value added by manufacturing, and tenth in dollars reinvested in capital expenditures.

Of the more than $34 billion shipments in printing and publishing in 1973, *commercial printing* accounted for over $10.1 billion of which lithography represented 54% and letterpress 31%; *newspaper* and *magazine* production was over $12 billion of which letterpress was the major producer, but web offset is growing rapidly in the weekly and small to medium sized daily newspapers and special interest magazines; *book publishing* and *printing* was over $4.1 billion of which lithography represented 75%. These figures do not include *packaging* which totaled $25.5 billion in shipments in the U.S. in 1973.

At the present time, the printing industry breaks down as follows in value of products produced: letterpress 50%, lithography 35%, gravure 10%, screen printing and other processes 5%. Lithography, especially web offset, is expected to grow in the 1970's at the expense of letterpress. The future is bright. As an industry, printing and publishing has a growth rate comparable to the gross national product, or about 5% per year. Offset lithography, book printing, color printing and gravure are growing at about twice this rate, while web offset and screen printing have been mushrooming at almost three times this rate. Lithography is projected to grow 15% per year in commercial printing over the next ten years.

In the 1980's lithography is expected to level off and gravure to grow at a rate comparable to lithography's growth in the 70's. The reasons for this are the many developments being made in gravure such as electromechanical engraving, electrostatic assist and water-based inks, which will make gravure an economical process for runs as low as 50,000 impressions so there will be some overlap in the run category from 50,000 to 200,000 between gravure and lithography.

Today's printer owes much to the Age of Science and to electronics, chemistry, optics and mechanics. Modern printing is becoming highly scientific. Specialized presses, inks, papers and techniques have been developed to meet every need. New plastics, electronic sensors, lasers, computer techniques and other products of modern research are being applied to printing and gradually converting it from an art to a science.

Recent printing developments include such advanced equipment as phototypesetting systems; direct screening; electronic scanners; automatic processors for films and press plates; new photopolymers for offset and letterpress plates; electromechanical engraving machines for gravure cylinders; presses that print a complete book in one pass through the press; and completely automated bindery machines. These are discussed in the following pages of the *Pocket Pal.*

THE FUTURE

Many new processes for recording data and producing images in quantity are being developed and used in duplicating and for computer printouts which may blossom into full-fledged printing processes some day. These include micropublishing, electrostatic, solid-state, and jet printing. In addition is facsimile transmission for all types of publishing. Some are in limited use now. Others could take many years before they could be considered serious contenders for a share of the printing market.

Facsimile Transmission

Long distance facsimile transmission is finding a use in the printing industry as a connection between the printers and their customers. Facsimile systems can transport copies and proofs cross-country almost instantly, and they could well replace the mails and messenger service as the primary link between printer and customer. It is already in use by The Wall Street Journal, McCall, McGraw-Hill, and W. A. Krueger Company as links between plants.

In magazine publishing, McGraw-Hill has introduced an interesting concept in which all type is photoset, and page layouts are composed in the publishing headquarters in New York. The punched tapes for the type and the page layouts are transmitted to the printing locations where the type is photoset and the magazines are printed. How soon it will be before the black and white and color illustrations are combined with the text and page layouts is a matter of time and cost, as all the hardware and most of the software for accomplishing this has already been developed. This could very well become the printing method of the future in which (1) all preparatory work (i.e. typesetting and illustrations) can be stored, ready for display or use, and (2) printing can be done at considerable distances depending on the quality of transmission.

Book publishing is also considering some new concepts that will revolutionize this old art. The author will compose on magnetic tape which will be transmitted and stored in a com-

AN ADVANCED FACSIMILE TRANSMISSION PRINTING SYSTEM

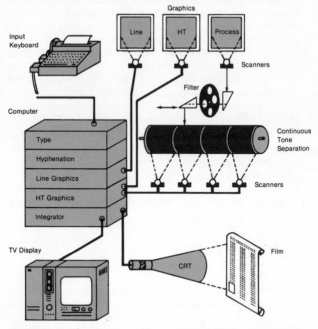

puter memory from which the editor, production manager, illustrator and art director can extract the copy and work on it. When the copy is complete it will be stored in page formats in the memory of the computer. The publisher, instead of trying to anticipate print orders for the book and inventorying them, will print on demand. Book stores will take orders for the book and direct them to a satellite printing plant in the area. The plant will contact the data bank in the computer which will transmit the page formats in sequential order so a complete book can be printed in each pass through the press. This type of printing without the need for assembling large signatures is being done now on Cameron Belt and Wood-Hoe Book-O-Matic presses, but the method is still somewhat cumbersome because of the plate system that has to be used. The new electrostatic or jet printing systems, as described later, could make this new book concept practical and economical.

Micropublishing

Micropublishing is an appreciable factor in the storage and retrieval of scientific and technical reports, directories, catalogs, medical and business records, engineering and architectural drawings, and even rare books in libraries. The industry is divided between aperture cards, roll film, and microfiche. Microfiche seems to be gaining in popularity because of the ease of designing readers and retrieving the information. Ordinary microfiche has about 30 normal size (8½″ x 11″) papers on a 4″ x 6″ film.

Ultra-microfiche, where reductions and magnifications from 75 to 200 times are necessary, has been used for special applications like the Ford Parts and Sears Catalogs, Commerce Clearing House Tax Library, etc., but these are not gaining at the rate of other micropublishing because of the extensive requirements for cleanliness in doing the photography.

Micropublishing can offer duplicating speeds of 650 pages per second and significant savings in mailing costs. It will certainly find a place in the printing and publishing industries, especially in the recording of information from computers, known as COM, and in the storage of reference materials in libraries.

Electrostatic Printing

One electrostatic printing process is that developed by Stanford Research Institute which electrostatically attracts dry toner through a screen stencil and is used to produce images on all sorts of odd-shaped objects like corrugated board, apples, avocados, plywood, nuts, pills, and even fried eggs.

A new variation of this process has been developed by The Electroprint Corporation in which holes in a bar can be controlled by a computer and charges transferred through selected holes into an ink cloud to cause ink droplets to be attracted to plain paper to form an image. As a printout device for computers, this process has been capable of printing 12,000 lines per minute which is about six times the speed of the best impact printers. The principles of this printer are being applied to the design of a copier, which could be used in the in-line concept of book printing.

Solid-State Printing

Solid-state printing utilizes an electroconductive drum which can be imaged or erased sequentially during printing. Recently, some new thin film, low-cost, amorphous, glass-like semi-conductors have been developed that can be used in a solid-state printer. A laser beam, directed by computer impulses, produces a pattern of latent charged images on a drum which are developed by toner and printed on paper. The images can be quickly erased and changed. This is one of the more promising systems so far proposed to accomplish an all-electronic printing system that can go directly from the computer to the printed sheet without process photography, stripping and platemaking. It fits ideally into the new concepts of book and magazine publishing. Because of the newness of the technology involved, development of this system will take a lot of time and money so we cannot expect to see much application of it in the 70's or even the 80's.

Jet Printing

Jet printing is a means of pressureless printing which creates an image with jets of colored material similar to fountain pen ink. The ink is sprayed through a nozzle under pressure, broken up into uniform droplets, charged electrically and deflected by a computer or other image generating device.

The process can be done in two ways. A single nozzle activated by a computer can oscillate back and forth over a sheet much as an electron-beam produces an image on a TV screen. This is the principle used in the A.B. Dick Videojet system. Coding equipment using this principle has produced non-contact printing of more than 1,300 characters per second on containers and packaging materials. The system has also been used to address more than a million U.S. income tax forms at the same time they were being printed on a web press running at 700 feet per minute.

The other method of jet printing is to use a bank of nozzles, each of which is digitally controlled by a computer program. As many as 200 to 300 jets per inch are used that can form droplets at speeds as high as 80,000 per second and can image 150,000 characters per second or 70,000 lines of type a minute. This is the basis of the system known as the Dijit Printer.

The American Newspaper Publishers Association has discussed with Massachusetts Institute of Technology the development of a method of plateless printing for producing newspapers. Jet printing, especially the Dijit Printer, as well as electrostatic processes are being considered. It will be interesting to follow the course of this project as its results can have a tremendous impact on the future of all types of printing and publishing.

While printing will probably change more in the next 20 years than it has in the over 500 years since Gutenberg, contrary to the predictions of McLuhan and other prophets of doom, the printed word will survive and continue to flourish. It is certain to change in the way it is produced, but it will be around for many years for people to read and admire.

the printing
processes

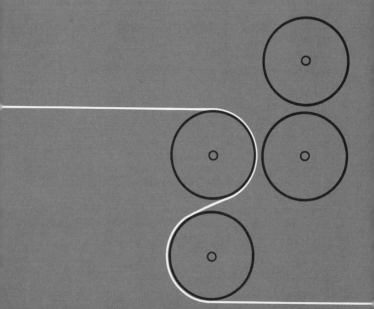

Four major processes are used in printing: letterpress, gravure, offset-lithography, and screen. Each uses a different method: letterpress is relief, gravure is intaglio, lithography is planographic, and screen is porous or stencil printing. Some office duplicating and electrostatic printing use modifications of these methods.

LETTERPRESS (Relief)

GRAVURE (Intaglio)

OFFSET (Planographic)

SCREEN (Porous or Stencil)

LETTERPRESS

This is the oldest and most versatile method of printing. There is equipment for short, medium or long runs; it is used for job and commercial printing, books, newspapers, magazines, as well as packaging printing and many types of specialty printing.

Letterpress is printed by the *relief* method. It is the only process which can use type directly. Printing is done from cast metal type or plates on which the image or printing areas are raised above the non-printing areas. Ink rollers touch only the top surface of the raised areas; the surrounding (non-printing) areas are lower and do not receive ink. The inked image is transferred directly to the paper.

Inasmuch as letterpress is the only process where printing can be done directly from type, this makes it economical for jobs consisting mainly of reading matter such as price lists, parts lists, directories, rate schedules, timetables and legal work. Changes can be readily made, and the type can be kept 'standing', ready to be used again for reprints.

Much time is consumed in *makeready* (building up of the press form so that both the light and heavy areas print with the correct impression). Highlights and shadows may be the same height, but the highlights exert more pressure than the shadows so that pressure must be relieved in the highlights and more pressure added in the shadows or heavy printing areas.

There are three types of presses: platen, flat-bed cylinder, and rotary. These are described in detail on pages 120-122.

On platen and flat-bed cylinder presses, the type or plates are mounted on a flat surface that forms the printing member of the press. Type and flat plates cannot be used on rotary presses; the printing member is a cylinder, and plates must be curved.

Printing is done on sheets of paper on sheet-fed presses, or rolls of paper on web-fed presses. Sheet-fed letterpress on small platen and flat-bed cylinder presses is used for short run printing such as letterheads, billheads, envelopes, announcements, invitations, and small advertising brochures. Larger sheet-fed letterpress is used for general printing, books, catalogs, advertising, and packaging. Web letterpress is used for newspapers and magazines.

Distinctive feature for recognizing letterpress is a heavier ring of ink around each letter (seen with a magnifying glass). The ink tends to spread slightly from the pressure of the plate upon the printed surface. Sometimes a slight embossing (denting) appears on the reverse side of the paper. The letterpress image is usually sharp and crisp.

Flexography

Flexography is a form of rotary web letterpress using flexible rubber plates and fast-drying solvent or water-based inks. The

HOW TO RECOGNIZE THE PRINTING PROCESSES

LETTERPRESS	GRAVURE	OFFSET
(Ring of Ink)	(Serrated Edges)	(Smooth Edges)

rubber plates are mounted to the printing cylinder with double-faced adhesive. Plates are sometimes backed with thin brass or other metal sheets and attached to the cylinder with fastening straps for close register.

Most anything that can go through a web press can be printed by flexography. Printing by the flexographic process ranges from decorated toilet tissue to bags, corrugated board and materials such as foil, hard-calendered papers, cellophane, polyethylene and other plastic films. It is well suited for printing large areas of solid color. Inks can be overlaid to obtain high gloss and special effects. With some types of papers having excessively high absorptive quality, flexography is uneconomical because of the fluidity of the ink. However, inks can be formulated to prevent too rapid absorption.

The growth of flexography for printing flexible films is almost synonymous with the expansion of the packaging industry and the development of the central impression cylinder press. Halftones as fine as 150 lines per inch have been printed on flexible films. It is also gaining prominence in the printing of business forms, books, folding cartons and corrugated boxes, as well as many specialty items from drinking straws to shower curtains. It is the major process for printing milk containers. Because of its color brilliance, flexography is used extensively in the printing of gift wraps and shopping bags.

Thermography (Raised Printing)

Thermography is a process which creates special effects in printing such as stationery, invitations, greeting cards, and paper decoration. A raised surface of printing resembling genuine engraving is formed without using costly engraving dies. Special non-drying inks are used in conventional printing, either by letterpress or offset, and the wet inks are dusted with a powdered compound. After the excess powder on the non-printing areas is removed by suction, the sheet passes under a heater which fuses the ink and powdered compound. The printing swells or *raises* in relief to produce a pleasing engraved effect.

GRAVURE

Whereas letterpress uses a *raised* (relief) surface, gravure uses a sunken or *depressed* surface for the image. Gravure is an example of intaglio printing. The image areas consist of cells or wells etched into a copper cylinder or wraparound plate, and the cylinder or plate surface represents the non-printing areas. The plate cylinder rotates in a bath of ink. The excess is wiped off the surface by a flexible steel *doctor blade*. The ink remaining in the thousands of recessed cells forms the image by direct transfer to the paper as it passes between the plate cylinder and the impression cylinder.

Gravure printing is considered to be excellent for reproducing pictures, but high plate-making expense usually limits its use to long runs. A distinctive feature for recognizing gravure is that the entire image must be screened—type and line drawings—as well as halftones. The gravure screen usually contains 150 lines per inch, about the same screen ruling as used in other processes. It is virtually invisible to the naked eye.

PRINCIPLE OF GRAVURE

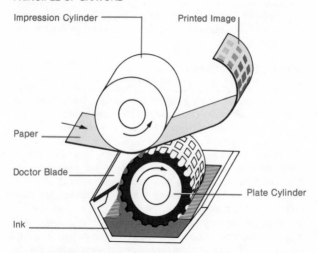

There are three types of gravure: conventional, variable area-variable depth, and direct transfer or variable area. These are described on pages 115-116. Conventional gravure is used for high quality printing. Variable area-variable depth is used for newspaper supplement, magazine and catalog printing. Variable area is used mainly for packaging.

As with rotary letterpress, gravure presses are manufactured both for sheets (sheet-fed gravure) and rolls (rotogravure) of paper, but most gravure is printed from rolls. Sunday newspaper magazine sections or supplements, color preprints for newspapers, premium stamp catalogs, large mail order catalogs, wallpaper, plastic laminates and postage stamps are common examples of rotogravure printing.

Steel-Die Engraving

In steel-die engraving, the surface of the die is hand or machine cut, or chemically etched where it is intended to hold ink. The plate is inked so that all sub-surfaces are filled with ink. Then the surface is wiped clean, leaving ink only in the depressed (or sunken) areas of the plate. The paper is slightly moistened and forced against the plate with tremendous pressure, drawing the ink from the depressed areas. This produces the characteristic embossed surface, while smoothing the paper immediately surrounding the impression. A slightly indented impression is left on the back.

Copper plates are used for short runs of one-time use (invitations and announcements). For longer or repeat runs such as letterheads, envelopes, greeting cards, stamps and money, both chromium-plated copper and steel plates are used in a die-stamping press.

OFFSET LITHOGRAPHY

This is the fastest growing of the four major printing processes. Lithography uses the *planographic* method. The image and non-printing areas are essentially on the same plane of the surface of a thin metal plate, and the definition between them is maintained chemically. Printing is from a *plane* or flat surface, one which is neither raised nor depressed. Two basic differences between offset lithography and other processes are: (1) it is based on the principle that grease and water do not mix, and (2) ink is *offset* first from plate to rubber blanket, and then from blanket to paper.

When the printing plate is made, the printing image is rendered grease receptive and water repellent, while the non-printing areas are rendered water receptive and ink repellent. On the press the plate is mounted on the plate cylinder which, as it rotates, comes into contact successively with rollers wet by a water or dampening solution, and rollers wet by ink. The dampening solution wets the non-printing areas of the plate and prevents the ink from wetting these areas. The ink wets the image areas which are transferred to the intermediate blanket cylinder. The paper picks up the image as it passes between the blanket cylinder and the impression cylinder.

Transferring the image from the plate to a rubber blanket before transfer to the paper is called the *offset principle*. Most lithography is printed in this way, and the term *offset* has become synonymous with lithography. Letterpress and gravure can also be printed by the offset principle.

One major advantage of the offset process is the fact that the soft rubber surface (as compared to letterpress metal plates) creates a clearer impression on a wide variety of paper surfaces and other materials with both rough and smooth textures. Offset lithography also allows extensive use of illustrations economically with a minimum of press makeready.

Offset printing can be recognized by a smooth print, as well as by the lack of any impression or ring of ink or serrated edge which are characteristic of letterpress and gravure *(see illustration, page 29)*.

PRINCIPLE OF OFFSET LITHOGRAPHY

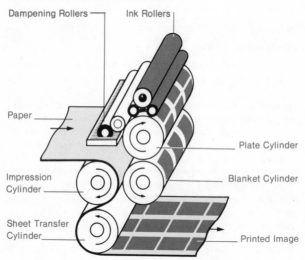

Dampening Rollers — Ink Rollers

Paper

Impression Cylinder

Sheet Transfer Cylinder

Plate Cylinder

Blanket Cylinder

Printed Image

Like letterpress, offset lithography has equipment for short, medium and long runs. Both sheet-fed and web-fed presses are used. Sheet-fed lithography has a broad range of printing including advertising, books, catalogs, greeting cards, posters, labels, packaging, folding boxes, decalcomanias, coupons, trading stamps, and art reproduction. Web offset is used for printing business forms, newspapers, preprinted newspaper inserts, advertising literature, catalogs, books, encyclopedias, and magazines.

Collotype

Collotype or photogelatin printing reproduces illustrations in continuous tone. Until recently it was the only printing process that is screenless. Screenless printing has also been done with special lithographic plates.

Collotype is a reproduction process which uses bichromated gelatin as a printing medium and is capable of high quality reproduction. It is used in runs from 100 to 5,000 and in sizes from 8"x10" to 44"x64". Platemaking is extremely critical compared with most other printing processes.

All types of original copy can be used ... color transparencies, colored art, photographs, drawings, etc. Posters are printed on one side on a wide variety of stock including coated paper. Transparencies are printed two sides on either paper or vinyl for back-lighted displays. Collotype is also used for fine art reproductions as well as outdoor bus and truck posters, banners, mounted displays, counter cards and floor displays.

SCREEN PRINTING

Formerly known as silk screen, this method employs a *porous* stencil. A fine silk, Nylon, Dacron, or stainless steel screen is mounted on a frame. A stencil is produced on the screen, either manually or photomechanically, in which the non-printing areas are protected by the stencil. Printing is done on a simple press by feeding paper under the screen, applying ink with a paint-like consistency to the screen, and spreading and forcing it through the fine mesh openings with a rubber squeegee.

Screen printing usually can be recognized by the thick layer of ink and the texture of the screen on the printing. This heavy film of ink may be controlled by the mesh of the stencil, the ink itself, or by various additives. The production rate, formerly limited by the drying time of the ink, has been greatly increased

PRINCIPLE OF SCREEN PRINTING

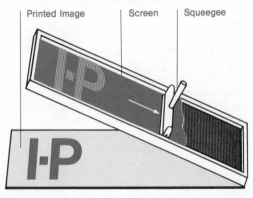

Printed Image   Screen   Squeegee

through the development of automatic presses and improved dryers. Recently, rotary screen presses have been introduced which speed up production considerably because they allow continuous operation.

Versatility is the principal advantage of screen printing. Any surface can be printed—wood, glass, metal, plastic, fabric, cork, etc.—in any shape or design, any thickness, and in any size. In advertising, screen printing is used for banners, decals, posters, 24-sheet billboards, car cards, displays, menu covers, etc. Heavy paperboards can be printed, eliminating costly mounting. Wallpapers and draperies are printed because of the depth of colors afforded—especially in the short-run custom designs of interior decorators. There are many new uses for screen printing, such as the printing of electronic circuits and decorating melamine plastic sheets before lamination.

COPIERS

Copying is sometimes referred to as *Reprography*. For less than 10 copies where high quality is not essential, the copier usually offers the fastest, most convenient and economical method of duplication. Copiers have been made using heat, light, electricity, chemical reactions, and combinations of these energy sources.

Thermography (or copying by heat—not to be confused with the printing process on page 30) was the first successful document copying process. This process, developed by 3M, uses a sheet consisting of a black infrared absorbing coating covered with a white coating. During exposure in contact with a document, a positive image is produced when the combination is subjected to infrared heat. An essential requirement for this process is that the text be written or printed with a substance which rapidly absorbs sufficient infrared radiation to activate the heat-sensitive coating. The white part of the original reflects most of the heat, but the black parts which constitute the image absorb and re-radiate the heat which activates the infrared absorbing coating removing the white coating from the image areas. Thus a black image is formed against a white background. The advantages of this system are that it is a single-step, dry method. No chemicals are required and the copy is made in about four seconds.

Electrophotography is the most common method used in copying today. There are plain paper and special paper electrophotographic copiers. Both types use electrophotographic coatings such as selenium or zinc oxide. These materials have the unique property of holding an electrostatic charge in the dark, and will lose the charge when exposed to the light reflected from the white areas of an original. The remaining charged areas which correspond to the image are developed with an oppositely charged dry powder or liquid ink called *toner*. The toner can be transferred from the electrophotographic copy onto plain paper by using electrostatic attraction. Dry toner images must be fixed by heat, pressure or solvent vapor. In the case of the transfer process, the electrophotographic coating is cleaned and can be re-imaged thousands of times.

The copier offers many special features such as push-button operation, enlargement or reduction, color copying, two side copies, automatic copy feed, copy counting, collating, and even imaging from microfilm.

Offset Duplicator

When copies in quantities above 10 up to 10,000 are needed, the most economical method for reproduction is usually the *offset duplicator*, which is essentially a small offset press and is described on page 129.

The **Copier/Duplicator** is an attempt at automation in duplicating as it combines the functions of a *copier* and a *duplicator*. The copier/duplicator employs an electrophotographic copier to make the plate, a transport system which automatically mounts the plate on the duplicator, treats it with a chemical, prints the number of copies programmed into the counter, rejects the old plate, and either turns itself off or inserts a new plate and continues to print. To simplify the operation of some copier/duplicators, the plates print directly onto the paper without using an intermediate offset blanket. This eliminates the need for cleaning the blanket between printings.

Other Duplicators—Stencil and Spirit

These two less expensive and less sophisticated systems for duplicating have been in use for many years. The *stencil duplicator*, or mimeograph, which works by forcing ink through a stencil usually prepared on a typewriter, produces copies of average quality on plain paper. The *spirit duplicator* is unique in that the master for it can be constructed to print more than one color at the same time. It is created using a special carbon paper which contains a soluble resin. A special printing paper is wet with a fast-drying solvent which, when brought in contact with the spirit master, softens and tackifies the resin so that a small amount of coloring dye is transferred to the paper. The master can be used over and over until all the ink is consumed which is usually about 100 prints.

type
and
typesetting

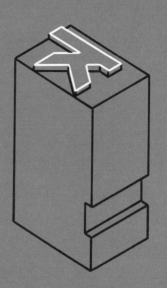

Printing can be defined as the reproduction in quantity of words and pictures on a page. In the photo-mechanical processes such as offset, any original camera-ready material to be printed is referred to as *copy* by the printer. Copy consists of all material to be reproduced in text or picture form. The term can be confusing however because "copy" is also used to refer to *manuscript copy*, which is the author's manuscript to be set in type. This section will deal with text copy, or type, and describe the various methods of typesetting.

TYPE FUNDAMENTALS

Type faces are usually available in 6 to 72 point, with a complete *font* in each size. A font is defined as a complete assortment of any one size and style of type containing all the characters for setting ordinary composition.

Capital letters are called *upper case* and small letters, *lower case*. These designations originated because the type was kept in two different cases. When the old-time compositors set type by hand, they placed the case with the capital letters above the case with the small letters, thus the name upper case.

In lower case letters the upper stroke (as in the letter "b") is called the *ascender,* and the downward stroke (as in "p") is known as the *descender.* The short crossline at the end of the main stroke is called the *serif.* The *body* or *x-height* makes up the greatest portion of a letter.

Ascender —
X-Height —
Descender —

Type size is measured from the top of an ascending letter to the bottom of a descending letter. The face of any letter is not the full point size. For example, the face of a 36-pt. letter may measure only 30 points.

Corresponding letters in the same size type may vary in height. For example, the following are all 24-pt. lower case "h":

h **h** h **h** h **h** h **h** **h** h

To most people, many type faces look alike; even an expert must look carefully to differentiate between them. While there is no short cut in learning how to identify type faces, careful study

HELVETICA MEDIUM IN 11 DIFFERENT SIZES

6 ABCDEFGHIJKLMNOPQRSTUVWXYZABCDEFG
8 ABCDEFGHIJKLMNOPQRSTUVWXYZ
10 ABCDEFGHIJKLMNOPQRSTU
12 ABCDEFGHIJKLMNOPQR
14 ABCDEFGHIJKLMNOP
18 ABCDEFGHIJKLM
24 ABCDEFGHI
30 ABCDEFG
42 ABCDE
48 ABCD
60 ABC

of a few key letters helps. For example, the lower case "g" is one of the most distinctive letters. The elements of this letter are: the top loop, the lower loop, the hook off the top loop, and the element joining the two loops. By studying the size, shape and position of these elements, the identity of the type face can be more easily determined. Other distinctive letters are: "p" "a" "e" and "t".

The entire appearance of a printed piece can be affected by the selection of type faces. Many characteristics – masculinity, femininity, delicacy, formality, etc. – can be suggested by the type face used. The guidance of a qualified designer, printer or typographer in selecting the proper type face is indispensable.

Above all, remember type was designed to be read easily! Both the selection of the type face and the size to be used must

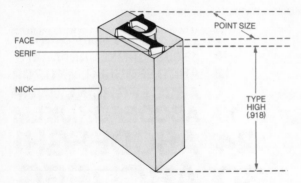

be considered. Use italics with care! Their primary purpose is for emphasis, not to be read in a mass.

CLASSIFICATION OF TYPE FACES

There are many approaches to type classification, none of which is precise. The following, however, is a useful breakdown covering a wide variety of type faces:

Oldstyle This type style group, patterned after letter forms used on classical Roman inscriptions, looks better in mass than when examined letter by letter. The letters have high readability because they are open, wide and round, with pointed serifs that make a pleasing contrast between the heavy and light strokes. Garamond and Caslon are examples.

Modern The term *modern* refers not to a time period, but to a style of type designed almost 200 years ago. These types have a much greater degree of mechanical perfection than Oldstyle faces and are distinguished by extreme contrast between thick and thin strokes. Times Roman and Caldonia are examples.

Square Serif A contemporary type style used mainly for display, headlines, and small amounts of reading matter. The letters have square or blocked serifs and more or less uniform strokes, and the face is even in texture and weight with very little contrast. Clarendon and Cairo are examples.

Sans Serif This type enjoys great popularity because of its simplicity of design. The letters have no serifs, and the face is generally even in overall weight with very little contrast between thick and thin strokes. Helvetica, News Gothic and Futura are examples. (The *Pocket Pal* is set in Helvetica.)

Script Designed to simulate handwriting, script type is used mostly for special effects, formal invitations, and announce-

ABCDEFGHIJKLMNOPQRSTUVW
abcdefghijklmnopqrstuvwxyzabcdefghij
OLD STYLE   GARAMOND

ABCDEFGHIJKLMNOPQRSTUV
abcdefghijklmnopqrstuvwxyzabcdefg
MODERN   TIMES ROMAN

ABCDEFGHIJKLMNOPQRST
abcdefghijklmnopqrstuvwxyza
SQUARE SERIF   CLARENDON

ABCDEFGHIJKLMNOPQRSTUVWX
abcdefghijklmnopqrstuvwxyzabcde
SANS SERIF   HELVETICA

ABCDEFGHIJKLMNOPQRS
abcdefghijklmnopqrstuvwxyzabcdefg
SCRIPT   COMMERCIAL SCRIPT

ABCDEFGHIJKLMNOPQRSTU
abcdefghijklmnopqrstuvwxyzabcdefg
TEXT LETTERS   OLD ENGLISH

ABCDEFGHIJKLMNOPQR
abcdefghijklmnopqrstuvw
DECORATIVE   COMSTOCK

ments. There are no serifs or extreme contrast between the thick and thin strokes, and the letters seem to touch each other. Commercial Script and Bank Script are examples.

Text Letters This group resembles the hand-drawn letters of the early scribes. It is usually selected for religious documents, certificates, diplomas and invitations, and is rarely used otherwise. Old English and Engravers Text are examples.

Decorative Types These are novelty styles or faces and used primarily to command attention. They are generally contemporary faces and do not fit any of the standard classifications. Designed to express different moods, they may be eccentric in appearance.

Type Families

Some types have many variations, and these various styles are said to be in the same family. Examples of these variations in a type style are: light face, medium, bold, extra bold, italic, expanded, and condensed.

A FAMILY OF TYPE

Helvetica Light

Helvetica Light Italic

Helvetica Regular

Helvetica Regular Italic

Helvetica Medium

Helvetica Medium Italic

READABILITY AND LEGIBILITY

Most people who are not concerned with the fine points of typography use readability and legibility synonymously. But there is a distinct difference: readability is the ease of reading a printed page, whereas legibility refers to the speed with which each letter or word can be recognized. Readability refers to the type arrangement; legibility is concerned with type design.

Readability and legibility are dependent upon several factors that must be considered when selecting a type face. These include texture and finish of paper, color of ink, size of type, line length, line spacing, etc. Type should be set to be read with little effort or eyestrain. Proper line spacing is important to the appearance of an ad or a printed piece. Each job presents a different problem, depending on the type style used, whether capital letters or lower case letters are to be used, etc. A good type designer will give that little extra service, in the best interests of his customer, to be sure that the spacing enhances the typography. In practice, good spacing is often a matter of common sense.

Letterspacing This is the amount of space between letters, either for readability or to fill a certain area. It is used mostly in capital letters for display. Caps and lower case as well as italic should not be letterspaced. Some lines require corrective letterspacing to make all letters appear optically evenly spaced.

NO LETTERSPACING

LETTERSPACING IS THE AMOUNT OF

2 POINT LETTERSPACING

LETTERSPACING IS THE AM

4 POINT LETTERSPACING

LETTERSPACING IS THE

Line spacing The amount of space between lines is known as leading and is always expressed in points. There is no set rule to follow. Too much leading can sometimes be as bad as not enough. Type faces with long ascenders and descenders require more leading. Also, the wider the measure of text composition, the more leading is required for good readability.

NO LINE SPACING

The amount of space between lines is known as leading. There is no set rule to follow. Too much leading can sometimes be as bad as not enough. Type faces with

1 POINT LINE SPACING

The amount of space between lines is known as leading. There is no set rule to follow. Too much leading can sometimes be as bad as not enough. Type faces with

2 POINT LINE SPACING

The amount of space between lines is known as leading. There is no set rule to follow. Too much leading can sometimes be as bad as not enough. Type faces with

3 POINT LINE SPACING

The amount of space between lines is known as leading. There is no set rule to follow. Too much leading can sometimes be as bad as not enough. Type faces with

PRINTERS' MEASUREMENTS

The *point* and the *pica* are two units of measure universally used in printing in most English-speaking countries. Their use is primarily in typesetting. Type size is measured in points. Line length measure is in picas and points. The pica is used to express overall width or depth as well as the length of a line.

The point measures .0138 or approximately 1/72 of an inch. In other words, there are 72 points to the inch. All type is designated in points (10-point Caslon, 24-point Baskerville, etc.). Points are always used to specify the *size* of type. Type faces are made in sizes from 4 to 144 points, but are generally used in 6 to 72 points. Line-spacing material such as leads and slugs are also specified in points (2-point lead, 6-point slug, etc.).

The pica is used for *linear* measurements of type. (A pica gauge is the printer's measuring tool.) There are 12 points to 1 pica, or 6 picas to 1 inch. The length of a line is specified in

PRINTERS' PICA GAUGE

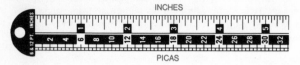

picas, as well as the depth of a type area. For example, a given block of copy is to be set 20 picas wide by 36 picas deep. Inches are never used in type measurement.

The em is also important in typesetting although not a part of the point system. It is the square of the type size (a 10-pt. em is 10 points wide and 10 points high) and is used for measuring the *quantity* of type. For example, a 3-inch line is 216 points long, and if set in 12-point type contains 18 ems of 12-point type (216 ÷ 12 = 18). The most common use of the em space today is that of paragraph indention.

The agate line is a measurement used by newspapers to sell advertising space. There are 14 agate lines to an inch. An agate line refers to the space occupied by one line of agate type in one column. The width of the column can vary from paper to paper. A 60 line ad can take several forms: 60 agate lines in one column; 30 agate lines in 2 columns, etc.

PROOFREADERS' MARKS

The proofreaders' marks shown on the following pages are standard and should be familiar to everyone working with type. It is important to use these accepted signs, rather than others which will not be understood by the typesetter. Marking changes with a colored pen or pencil enables the typesetter to see the corrections more easily. The illustration on page 47 shows how these symbols are used in actual practice.

Delete and Insert

℮	Delete, take out!
℮	Delete and closeup
l/s	LETTER SP A CE
#	Insert space(more space)
□	Em quad space or indention
stet	Let it stand—(all matter above dots)

Punctuation Marks

⊙	Period
⋏	Comma
⑆	Semicolon
⊙	Colon
⌵	Apostrophe or 'single quote'
⌶	Open quotes
⌶	Close quotes
?/	Question mark
!/	Exclamation point
=	Hyphen
(/)	Parentheses
/—/	Dash

Style of Type

wf	Wrong style of type
lc	Set in LOWER CASE or LOWER CASE
caps	SET IN capital letters
caps+lc	Lower case with Initial Caps
sc	SET IN small capitals
rom	Set in roman type
ital	Set in italic type

lf Set in (**light face**) type

bf **Set in** bold face **type**

Spacing

⊃ Close up en tirely; take out space

⌣ Less space between words

Insert space

Paragraphing and Position

⊐ Move to right ⊐

⊏ ⊏ Move to left

⊔ Lower (letters or words)

⊓ Raise (letters or words)

= Align horizontally

‖ Align vertically

¶ Begin a paragraph

no ¶ No paragraph.

run in Run in

flush ¶ ←No paragraph indention

tr Transpose letters in a word

tr Transpose enclosed in circle (matter)

Miscellaneous

✕ Broken type

⑨ Invert (upside-down type)

↓ Push down space

(sp) Spell out (Capt) Smith)

ok ʷ/c OK "with corrections"

ok ᵃ/c or "as corrected"

⌄∙∙∙⌄ Ellipsis

Proof with Errors Marked

THE PRACTICE OF TYPOGRAPHY, if it eb followed
faithfully, is hard work—full of detail, full petty
restrictions full of drudgery, and not Greatly
rewarded as men now count rewards: There are
times when we need to bring to it, all the history
and art and feeling that w can, to make it bearable.

But in the light of history and of art, and of
knowledge and of mans achievement, it is as
interesting a work as exists—a broad and
humanizingemployment which can *indeed* be
followed merely as a trade, but which if perfected into an art, or even broadened into a profession, will perpetually open new horizons to
eyes our and opportunities to our hands.

—D. B. Updike

Proof after Corrections Have Been Made

THE PRACTICE OF TYPOGRAPHY, if it be followed
faithfully, is hard work—full of detail, full of petty restrictions, full of drudgery, and not greatly
rewarded as men now count rewards. There are
times when we need to bring to it all the history
and art and feeling that we can, to make it
bearable. But in the light of history, and of art,
and of knowledge and of man's achievement, it is
as interesting a work as exists—a broad and
humanizing employment which can indeed be
followed merely as a trade, but which if perfected
into an art, or even broadened into a profession,
will perpetually open new horizons to our eyes
and opportunities to our hands.   —D. B. UPDIKE

TYPESETTING

After the different characteristics and styles of type are known, it is important to be familiar with the various methods of typesetting. There are three basic methods of producing type: cast metal or hot type composition, typewriter or direct-impression composition (also referred to as strike-on or cold type), and phototypesetting. Hot type refers to cast metal type whether it is set by hand or machine. Continuing development has widened the choice of typesetting methods to be used, especially in phototypesetting.

Hand Composition

Hand-set composition is produced with individual metal characters assembled into lines much as Gutenberg did in 1450. A *composing stick* is held in one hand while the letters are selected from a type case with the other and placed in the stick

COMPOSING STICK

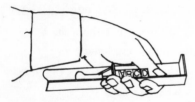

until a full line is set. Different size spaces are then used to *justify* the line, filling it out to the desired width. This is repeated until all the copy has been set. For line spacing, or when an exact depth is wanted for a block of type, metal strips or slugs are inserted between the lines. The process of returning the type to the case is called *distribution*. At best, hand composition is slow and is used for small amounts of type, primarily larger sizes for headings.

Hand-set type is not commonly used for direct reproduction. Either a duplicate plate is made for letterpress printing, or inked proofs (reproduction proofs) are made which are later photographed for use in other methods of printing.

Machine Composition

Machine-set copy can be produced on any of four machines. The Linotype and Intertype machines cast a line of type at a time; the Monotype system produces individual characters; and the Ludlow machine, which also casts one line of type at a time, is used mainly for display type or headlines.

LINECASTING MACHINE

Caster   Keyboard   Magazine

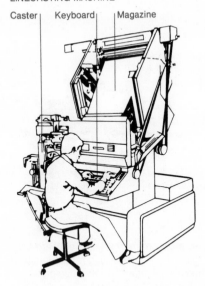

Linotype, Intertype machines cast a one-piece line of type to a predetermined length. The operator sits at a typewriter-like keyboard. At the touch of a key, a *matrix* is released from a *magazine* (storage case). Once all the matrices (characters) for one line are assembled, the line is automatically justified by special *spacebands.* The operator then pushes a lever which moves the line into the casting mechanism. From there, the line is handled automatically, and the operator begins to set the next line. After the first line has been cast and the slug ejected from the mold, the matrices are returned to the magazine, ready to be used again. Each size of each type face has its own magazine.

Some linecasting machines have been equipped for semi-automatic operation from perforated tape. These tape-controlled systems, such as the *Teletypesetter,* allow one operator to handle the production of several linecasters. The tape, which can be prepared in-house on tape perforators or received over wire services, is used mostly by newspapers for financial material, box scores, etc. With tape-controlled linecasting, the machine output is greatly increased. Maximum speed depends on the machine, and it takes several keyboard operators to keep one tape-controlled linecasting machine busy.

MONOTYPE SYSTEM

Keyboard   Typecaster

Monotype is a combination of two machines: a *keyboard* (perforator), and a *typecaster*. As the name suggests, Monotype casts the characters one by one rather than as a complete line. As the operator types the copy he automatically produces a perforated paper tape, which is used to drive the typecaster. To justify the lines of type, a counting mechanism automatically registers the widths of the characters as they are typed. When the maximum number of characters per line has been reached, a bell rings to alert the operator. He strikes a series of keys to determine how much additional space must be added to justify the line. Up to this point, no type has actually been set. We have only a perforated, or coded paper roll. To set the type, the roll is fed into the typecaster, where it drives the casting mechanism by means of compressed air.

Monotype is ideal for setting complicated tabular matter such as financial statements and charts. One advantage of Monotype is that many corrections can be made by hand, rather than costly machine time.

Ludlow This system is a semi-automatic method of typesetting, combining hand and machine composition. Individual matrices are assembled by hand in a special composing stick. The justified line is then inserted into the Ludlow machine, and mechanically cast into a slug. While this operation is similar to hand composition, the advantage is that a new slug is made for each line of type. This gives the printer an unlimited supply of type from one set of matrices. Ludlow is especially suitable for

LUDLOW COMPOSING STICK

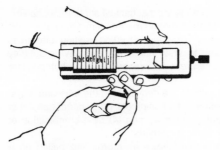

display type and headings. A variety of type styles and sizes from 6 to 144 point are available. Ludlow also makes a machine for casting line-spacing material and rules.

Press or Foundry Lockup

In letterpress and conversion to photomechanical platemaking, type is locked up in a *chase* (a heavy rectangular steel frame). Lockup is done on a large table called a *stone,* so named because originally it had a stone top; today the top is steel. The form does not take up the entire area inside the chase, and the empty spaces are filled up with *furniture* (wood or metal blocks). In addition to the furniture, *quoins* (steel wedge-shaped devices) are placed on two adjacent sides of the form between the furniture. The quoins are tightened slightly, and the form is planed for levelness. Once all the parts are made level, the quoins are tightened to hold the form securely in place.

CHASE Furniture Type Quoins

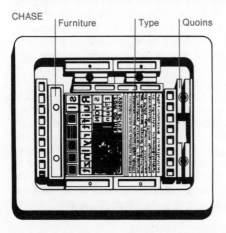

IMAGE CONVERSION SYSTEMS

Image conversion systems are mechanical or photomechanical processes for converting metal type into film. Originally, such systems were used primarily for converting existing letterpress plates and type forms to offset lithography and gravure, but they are now used in letterpress for wraparound and photopolymer plates.

Relief image carriers are converted in the following ways: (1) by pulling inked reproduction proofs, (2) by direct transfer of the image, (3) photographically, and (4) by a combination of mechanical and chemical methods.

Reproduction proofs, known as *repros,* are pulled on a proof press. The relief matter is inked and transferred to a sheet of opaque, translucent or transparent material, such as coated paper which is opaque, glassine which is transparent, or plastic film which is either translucent or transparent. The quality must be carefully controlled.

A number of special materials have been developed for this purpose. One of them, *Scotchprint,* is a special plastic material which is highly ink receptive. The end product is a translucent positive which can be made into a negative by contact or by camera. *Converkal* is a direct image transfer method which converts type forms into reproduction negatives in normal room light without use of camera or darkroom. Converkal becomes a film negative instantly on proofpress contact to warmed type. After the type form is locked in a chase, it is heated, and a repro-negative is pulled.

Brightype is a photographic image conversion method. The type form or plate is first sprayed with a special non-reflecting black lacquer. The printing surface is then made reflective by burnishing with a rubber pad. A series of special revolving lights illuminate the polished surface which is photographed by a special camera. Positive film or paper is the end product.

Image conversion by combining mechanical with chemical methods requires neither ink nor camera. *Cronapress* is a non-photosensitive film with a white pressure-sensitive coating. After vacuum drawdown, thousands of small lead or steel balls are bounced at random over the film. The multiple impact of the balls converts the film into a right-reading negative of the form. It is then treated with a densifying agent and stabilizing solution which opaques the non-image areas.

With the continuing acceptance today of non-metallic forms of typesetting, the need for image conversion systems has decreased.

TYPEWRITER OR DIRECT-IMPRESSION COMPOSITION

This is usually referred to as *strike-on* or *cold type*, although the term has little significance. The ordinary typewriter produces rudimentary composition, but not enough to matter in commercial and in-plant typesetting. High-speed computer driven direct-impression machines produce large quantities of print on paper suitable for reproduction. However, with improved production capabilities and typographic appearance, high-speed electronic phototypesetters and cathode-ray-tube (CRT) equipment are gradually taking over a greater amount of typesetting.

Several machines are used in direct-impression composition. These are the VariTyper, the Friden Justowriter, and IBM's Selectric Composer (SC) system. All have proportionally designed type faces and produce justified composition.

VariTyper machines require double typing for justified composition, and can mix two fonts in the same line. After setting the carriage for a particular line length, the operator types the line until a signal indicates the line is within justification range. The operator tabs over and retypes the line at that time. The VariTyper word spacing mechanism automatically adds or subtracts space between words to permit justification.

The *Justowriter* system utilizes paper tape and two typing units. The recorder generates a perforated paper tape with line endings in justification range and a hard copy printout. The paper tape is then inserted into a reproducing unit which contains two readers. The tape is read and strike-on type produced automatically in a justified form on a reproduction grade paper.

IBM's *Selectric Composer,* like the VariTyper, is a single-unit machine that requires double typing for justified composi-

IBM MT SYSTEM

Recorder   Selectric Composer

tion. Because it carries a single "ball" font, it cannot set mixed composition in the same line without complicated ballchanging. The MT system is more sophisticated in operation and requires only a single typing. It consists of one or more recorders that produce unjustified copy and coded input magnetic tape. If the input is correct, the magnetic tape is processed, and a Selectric Composer sets justified composition. If there are corrections, these can be made on another magnetic tape, and the tape reader merges the correction tape with the original tape to produce the final composition.

PHOTOGRAPHIC TYPESETTING

Metal typesetting is gradually giving way to phototypesetting and other direct-imaging composition that reduces the number of production steps leading up to the complete page pasteup required in platemaking for every major printing process. Even letterpress is now using phototypesetting for photopolymer and other photomechanical plates.

Besides typewriter composition there are three types of direct-imaging processes:

(1) Phototypesetting of varying electronic sophistication, automation, imaging speed, and typographic versatility. Producing composition from simple straight matter to full-page, multi-column formats combining text and display, on photographic paper, film, or paper plates.

(2) Photolettering and Photo-display. This category covers equipment specifically oriented to the production of headline typesetting. The Filmotype, Protype, PhotoTypositor, Staromat and Visutek are examples.

(3) Transfer lettering, and *paper type.* This category includes manually manipulated materials used in simple character-by-character composition of words and lines for heads and display where production speed is not a factor.

These processes have a place in the new technology of composition. It is not unusual to find sophisticated phototypesetters together with hand-operated display equipment in the same composing room or printing department. In this case, perhaps the manual devices are used only for occasional display setting or for little-used type faces that are not considered utilitarian enough to include in the phototypesetter library. Whatever the equipment used, the direct-imaging process is gradually changing the over-all field of typesetting. Equipment is compact, quiet in operation, and easy to arrange for orderly work flow.

How Photographic Typesetting Works

All photographic typesetting requires three elements: a master character image, a light source, and a photo or light sensitive material. Phototypesetting systems have undergone three major evolutionary changes from the development of the first phototypesetting device.

First generation These units are adaptations of machine-set typesetting. The Fotosetter (introduced in 1950) is essentially an Intertype. The Monophoto is essentially a Monotype. In these machines the master character image is carried on the matrix. The matrix contains a negative of the character and is photographed instead of cast. First generation phototypesetters are mechanical in nature and use slower tungsten light sources.

Second generation These units are electro-mechanical in nature. The Photon 200B (introduced in 1954) was the first working device utilizing new technology. Today there are well over 100 models available from a dozen suppliers. Here is a diagram of a typical phototypesetter of this type.

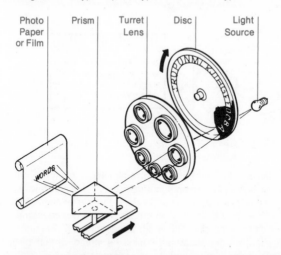

Photo Paper or Film | Prism | Turret Lens | Disc | Light Source

Third generation These units utilize cathode ray tube technology and are totally electronic. Characters are formed on the screen of a high resolution CRT (TV tube) by a series of minute dots or lines. The resultant image is then transferred to photographic material. Because CRT typesetters set type with a beam of light they are capable of extremely high speeds (over 1,000 30-character 8-point lines in a minute).

Character Storage

All phototypesetters must store their master character sets in some form. These sets include all of the characters and symbols for a particular type style. VariTyper, and Intertype units utilize discs. Compugraphic and Star units utilize film strips. Mergenthaler's Linofilm and the Alphatype utilize grids. The

TYPE FONT CONFIGURATIONS

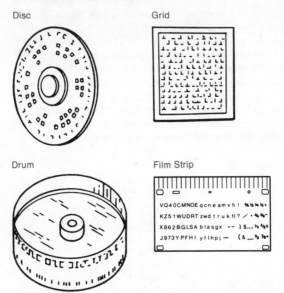

Disc

Grid

Drum

Film Strip

Mergenthaler V-I-P and Photon utilize film segments mounted on a drum. Some of these photomatrices may contain as few as one or as many as sixteen fonts. On some, the master character image is enlarged by lenses, on others the size on the matrix determines the type size. The width values for each character of every font on the photomatrix must be stored so that the photo output unit can properly space characters.

Photo Output Unit

Copy to be typeset is usually input to a phototypesetter by tape (although direct input by keyboard is also utilized). Characters are then selected by referencing certain marks on the photo-matrix which refer to certain characters. When the proper mark is reached a burst of light from a xenon flash lamp is exposed through the master character image. This beam of light is then deflected to the correct optical path by mirrors or prisms, enlarged by lenses and then positioned on photosensitive output material.

Optical Systems

Phototypesetters differ in their basic approach to imaging. Some use lenses (one for each size enlargement) that are mounted in a turret. Some use a zoom lens that *telescopes* to the particular enlargement size. Characters may be positioned by prisms, mirrors, lenses and fiber optic bundles that move on a track, or mirrors that rotate.

Imaging Speed

Phototypesetting speed is usually measured in newspaper lines per minute (lpm). A standard line is 8 point, 11 picas with 30 characters. Most second generation phototypesetters average 50 lpm with a high of 150 lpm. The speed of direct input machines, like hot metal linecasters, is determined by the speed of the operator.

CRT Typesetters

Third generation phototypesetters such as the Videocomp, Intertype Fototronic CRT, Mergenthaler Linotron 303 and 505, Compugraphic VideoSetter and MGD Metro-Set are capable of greatly increased speeds and can also in some cases, create complete pages of text and headline material *in position*. Characters are stored as either master images or as digital information and then translated into dot placement on the CRT screen.

In operation, as copy and typographic commands on paper tape or magnetic tape are read and analyzed, patterns of the needed characters are called out of the memory section and are imaged on the cathode ray tube in correct size at their precise positions in the page or format. It is this finished composition that is beamed from the tube to the photopaper, film, or offset plate material being used.

Though character images are solid and accurately contoured shapes after imaging and printing, they are actually patterns of characters, and consist of adjoining sweeps of scan lines, similar to the buildup of images on television screens. The density of these scan lines to the inch determines the typographic quality of the imaged characters and the imaging speed of any particular CRT system. The more scan lines to the inch, the higher the resolution (sharpness) of the characters. The less scan lines to the inch, such as in a proof mode, the lower the resolution and the faster the output.

Shown here is a simplified, enlarged and outlined diagram of one CRT system's pattern buildup of a 9-point character. Imagine that each outlined bar is a solid black bar or line. It takes

62 of these scan lines in less than 1/16″ to image this 9-point character. In this outlined diagram, the solid scan lines merge optically to form a smoothly contoured character that is as sharp to the eyes as a similar character imaged in a single flash inside a regular phototypesetter or printed from the face of metal type. To simulate the optical merging of scan lines, hold this page at arm's length and squint your eyes as you look at the pattern of the "B".

Typesetting Trends

Two trends have characterized modern typesetting development. The first is full page makeup (including halftones and drawings), and the second is dry output (no chemical processing). Lasers will play an important role in both areas. (The Associated Press LaserPhoto which is used to transmit halftones over telephone lines is indicative of the technology needed to create complete pages.)

Input

All phototypesetting devices must have some form of input. The major forms of input are:

Direct input Here the typesetting device is connected to a keyboard. Thus the speed of the typesetter is directly related to the input speed of the operator. Compugraphic's CompuWriter and Mergenthaler's Linocomp are examples of direct input phototypesetters.

Off-line keyboard This type of device produces a "record" of the information keyed, in the form of perforated paper tape or magnetic tape. In some cases, the operator may make the hyphenation and justification decisions. The keyboard is then called *counting* and the input *justified.* When no decisions are made by the input operator because the computer will hyphenate and justify, the keyboard is called *non-counting* and the input unjustified or *idiot.*

Optical character recognition (OCR) This new technology has the ability to take typewritten sheets and scan them to produce input to a computer-driven typesetter. The OCR machine *reads* the characters and then produces a paper tape or other form of input. Thus anyone who produces manuscript copy can now provide pages directly for input and thus avoid redundant rekeyboarding.

Video display terminals (VDT) These units also use CRTs. However, a VDT screen is used to show words (instead of pictures), and thus allows an operator to view the contents of an in-

VDT EDITING TERMINAL

put tape, and then to add, delete or change copy at will. A new corrected tape is produced.

Designed originally as an editing device, rapid changes in technology have made the VDT one of the more useful tools in today's phototypesetting department. Operators may now not only edit pre-keyboarded copy, but also do area makeup directly on the screen. Some VDTs allow tabular material to be shown on the screen exactly as it will be typeset, line for line, thus allowing the operator to check lineup and fit before actual typesetting. A few large newspapers are using VDTs in conjunction with mass storage devices as direct input to typesetters. Reporters and feature writers keyboard their articles directly into a VDT where they may see their article as it will appear in type. This material is then stored on magnetic discs or tapes.

Editors then call out this information on master VDTs, edit, format and send it directly to on-line typesetters, thus eliminating rekeyboarding. At the present time there are more than 50 manufacturers of VDTs.

Word processing (WP) The IBM MT/ST was the first word processor. It was essentially a typewriter with magnetic tape cartridges that allowed the operator to update and change input copy during or after typing.

Computerization

Computers are now applied to all areas of the typesetting process. Mini and micro computers are at work in OCR, VDT, WP, CRT and other devices. In phototypesetting units with computers or those that are run by external computers, the function of the *electronic brain* is the selection of characters and their proper positioning in response to input commands. A major function is the hyphenation and justification of lines of type from unjustified input.

Markup Since computerized phototypesetting can only act in response to input and input commands, it is the responsibility of the markup specialist to review manuscript copy and to add the computer codes that will be needed to do the typographic job at hand. Markup is called the *programming of typography*.

Photographic Output

Most phototypesetters expose photographic paper, film or an offset paper plate. Most users expose photo paper, either stabilization or true photomechanical. An inexpensive processor with two chemicals (activator and stabilizer) is used with stabilization paper. Tray development or more sophisticated processors are required for photomechanical or plate materials.

Page Assembly

Although all phototypesetting output is eventually assembled into paper or film mechanicals, the trend toward complete in-machine makeup has accelerated. This is essentially the difference between phototypesetting and photocomposition. The latter process, because of greater typographic capability, allows the production of complete page units (headlines, texts, footnotes, indents, etc.) in position. Thus it becomes possible to skip typesetting and perhaps go directly to some form of computer-controlled *printing* (electrostatics, ink jet, solid state, etc.)

copy
preparation
art
preparation

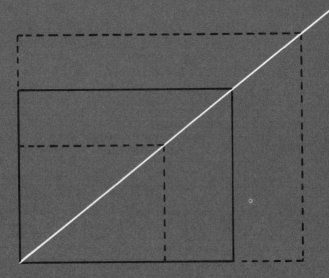

The mechanics of typesetting have already been discussed. This section will explain (1) how to prepare manuscript copy for typesetting, and (2) how to prepare art for graphic reproduction.

COPY PREPARATION FOR TYPESETTING

Good copy preparation and accurate markup insures correct typesetting of manuscript copy with a minimum of alterations, in the shortest possible time, and thus at the lowest cost.

Careful checking and editing of text matter *before* it is set is a must! Remember, the typesetter *must* set copy as it is furnished, even if he suspects errors. Therefore, it is of the utmost importance that spelling, punctuation, capitalization, uniformity of style, etc., be carefully checked.

The ground rules for good copy preparation, though established long ago, still apply today:

Paper Use standard 8½ x 11 letter size white bond. This allows for erasures and fits standard file cabinets.

Typing should be clean, double-spaced, of uniform length, with wide margins, and on one side only. Make a carbon or copy as insurance against loss of the original.

Identification should be made at the top of each sheet to prevent possible mixup – title, running head or any other helpful information.

Numbering Sheets should be numbered consecutively and mark *end* on the last sheet. If a sheet is added or removed after numbering, proper notation should be made on the preceding page.

Corrections should be made above the line wherever possible, in ink – not pencil. If there are many corrections, the page should be retyped. Corrections should *not* be made in the left margin, on the back of the sheet, or on attached slips which may be misplaced or lost.

Simplifying the typesetter's job helps to reduce costs and often expedites delivery. Corrections made in the manuscript are far less costly than *author's alterations* in type.

Copyfitting

Copyfitting refers to the amount of manuscript copy that can be fit into a given area of a printed piece for a specified size and style of type. Many different copy elements may occupy predetermined areas, and it is the task of the typographer to select the kind and size of type that will do the job best. Book composition presents a different problem in copyfitting. A length estimate is prepared (overall character count of the entire manuscript) and converted into point size, leading, pica measure and line count per page based on a predetermined estimated number of pages in the book.

There are different approaches to the problem of copyfitting. Sometimes the copy is specified in a given type face, size and measure. In this case, it is necessary to estimate the total number of lines paragraph by paragraph. This will determine the total depth of type, or the number of pages it will make.

When copy must be fitted into a given area, there are two basic steps to be taken: (1) the copy must be accurately measured, and (2) that measure must be applied to a specific size of a specific type face.

Copy measurement The *character count* method of measuring copy is the most accurate and widely used. This consists of counting the characters and spaces in the typewritten copy, line for line, on a paragraph basis. There are various aids for doing this. The handiest is a ruler calibrated in inches. Standard *pica* typewriters (12-point) have 10 characters to the inch, while the more common *elite* (10-point) have 12 characters to the inch. After the count is completed, the next step is to calculate the area into which it will fit in the selected type face.

Methods of type calculation There are type books that list the characters-per-pica of all sizes of the most common type faces. With these charts it is quite simple to calculate the number of characters in a desired size and pica measure of a given type face. By dividing this number into the total number of characters in the copy, paragraph by paragraph, one can determine the total number of lines the copy will make.

For example, if we know that a 20 pica line of 10-point Times Roman has 53 characters, and that the original copy contains 562 characters in one paragraph, by dividing 562 by 53 we get 10+ or 11 lines of type for that paragraph.

TYPICAL COPYFITTING TABLE

HELVETICA REG., Character Count Per Pica

Picas ▶	10	12	14	16	18	20	22	24	26	28	30
7 pt.	32	38	45	51	58	64	70	77	83	90	96
8 pt.	29	35	41	46	52	58	64	70	75	81	87
9 pt.	27	32	38	43	49	54	59	65	70	76	81
10 pt.	24	29	34	38	43	48	53	58	62	67	72
12 pt.	20	24	28	32	36	40	44	48	52	56	60

Copy Markup

The type specifications should be clearly and completely written on the typed manuscript (not the layout) with the size, leading, type face, and measure in that order. In marking the size, the leading (space between lines) should always be specified in the form of a fraction – 8/9 (8 on 9) means 8-point type with 1-point leading, 10/10 means 10-point solid (no leading), etc. Leading does not affect the number of lines, only the depth. When a large amount of copy is to be set, care should be used in selecting a type face that does not require a great deal of leading.

Always specify line measure in picas. An example of complete specifications would be: 10/12 Times Roman x 20, which means 10-point Times Roman with 2-point leading to be set 20 picas wide. Indicate if it is to be justified or set flush with a ragged right or left.

Careful word spacing is important! It must be remembered that all formulas for copyfitting are based on even word spacing throughout. If a job is widely word spaced, copyfitting calculations may be upset by poor workmanship.

All paragraph indentions, hold-ins, etc., should be indicated in *ems* of the type size – not in picas. (An *em* is the square of the body type, i.e., an 8-point em is 8 points square.) Be sure to indicate whether paragraphs should be indented or kept flush. Mark headings flush left, flush right, centered, and/or indented according to the design.

Underscoring a word or line has a very definite meaning to the typesetter. One underscore means *set in italic,* two mean SET IN SMALL CAPS and three underscores mean SET IN ALL CAPS. Underscore also means "underline" which is done with a rule by the typesetter or drawn on a repro, not to be confused with setting italic. Although a wavy underscore means **set in bold face,** it is always better to mark "bf" in the margin.

Again, in order to avoid delays and resetting, always mark up copy fully and accurately, then recheck your work. Accurate copy markup eliminates guessing and expedites delivery.

ART PREPARATION

Having discussed how to prepare manuscript copy for typesetting, the next consideration is art preparation. To the printer, art and copy (not to be confused with manuscript copy) are terms used to describe *all* material supplied for reproduction. It includes not only the type, but also diagrams, drawings, photographs, and color transparencies. Art preparation embraces all of the steps in getting the art and copy ready for reproduction. There are two basic steps: (1) the design or layout of a printed piece, and (2) the preparation and assembly of the various components of this piece for reproduction.

The Layout

The first step in the designing of a printed piece is preparing a layout ... a blueprint of a printed job. It is important that the layout person know the purpose of the printed piece (as well as the printing process to be used) so that the layout will reflect this. The layout may be a very rough visual, a semi-comprehensive, or a tightly rendered comprehensive, looking like the finished job in all details. The designer of a booklet or folder will often make several rough sketches (called *roughs)* of the cover and a two-page spread for approval. Then, once approved, often after many changes, proceed with the final layout. The final layout may be crudely drawn, but it must be accurate in size and accurately marked, as it is the blueprint from which all people (including the designer) who will be producing the job will take their specifications.

At the same time the layouts are being prepared, a blank paper dummy of the job should be made to size, preferably on the stock to be used. This will help the designer visualize the final appearance, enabling him to provide proper margins, bleeds, color, etc. Attention should be paid to stay within the boundaries of standard paper sizes and the printing process to be used.

With the approved layout and paper dummy to guide him, the artist is ready to put all the elements together into a final pasted up *mechanical* (or *pasteup)* for graphic reproduction.

ROUGH LAYOUT

COMPREHENSIVE LAYOUT

LINE HALFTONE

Kinds of Original Images

There are several kinds of original images. In general, they are classified according to whether the copy is *line* as in type matter, diagrams, and pen and ink drawings; or *continuous-tone* as in a black-and-white photograph with a variety of tones. These are further broken down as to whether they are to be reproduced in one color, multicolor, or process color, and whether they are alone or in combination (line and continuous-tone).

Therefore, we can have either line or continuous-tone images in one color, combinations of line and tone in one color; line or tone in more than one color, combinations of line and tone in more than one color; process color tone images, and combinations of process color tone and line.

Continuous-tone images may be either rendered illustrations or photographs. For reproduction by most printing processes, continuous-tone images are converted to dot pattern images, or *halftones*. Halftones have the appearance of continuous-tone images because of the limited resolving power of the human eye. This limitation accounts for an optical illusion; small halftone dots when viewed at the normal reading distance cannot be resolved as individual dots, but blend into a continuous tone. *(See illustration, next page.)*

Art for Multicolor Printing

Most art for multicolor reproduction is prepared in black and white on a mechanical. When hairline register is not required, the art for the key color is pasted to a sheet of illustration board, and the art for other colors registered on clear acetate overlays

MULTICOLOR MECHANICAL (2nd & 3rd colors on overlays)

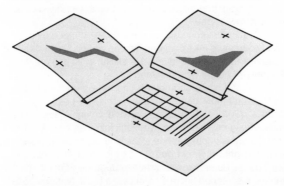

hinged to the board. Color and screened percentages (if any) should be marked on each overlay. This is sometimes called *pre-separated* art. For hairline register all colors should appear on the same board, and the color break indicated on a tissue overlay. Finish size should also be indicated on the art. If several pieces of art are prepared for a job, they should be drawn all the same size. This simplifies camera and preparation costs. All copy should be *keyed* or cross-referenced by page number, title or job number.

In preparing art where two or more colors are to be printed, registration of the different color images is usually an important factor. Where several color areas are completely independent of each other, it is considered a *no-register* job; *commercial register* means that slight variations in color images are incon-

HALFTONE DOTS ENLARGED

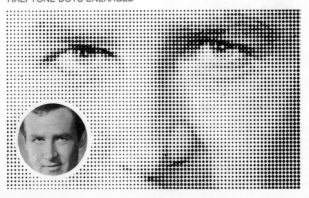

sequential (about ± one row of dots); *tight, close* or *hairline register* indicates that the relations must be extremely precise (± about ½ row of dots).

Additional colors and color values can be obtained by over-printing two or more inks. Overprinting can be in both solids and tints (various tones of a solid color). A skillful artist can create a wide variety of colors by this method.

A black-and-white photograph can be reproduced in two colors to obtain more depth or density. This two-color halftone is called a *duotone*. Two closely related colors, black and a complementary color, or even two black inks can be used. The original picture is photographed twice, one negative emphasiz-ing the highlights (lightest parts), and the other, the shadows (darkest parts). Sometimes, a two-color *duotone effect* is used, by printing a screened tint of a color over a black halftone. *(See illustrations, page 90.)*

Art for color reproduction falls into two classes: *reflection* and *transmission* copy. Reflection copy is original material for reproduction which is viewed and photographed by reflected light, such as oil paintings and photographic color prints.

REFLECTION COPY

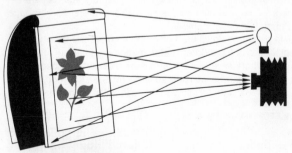

TRANSMISSION COPY

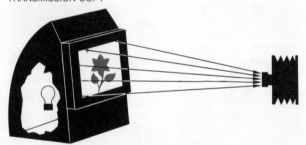

Transmission copy, such as color transparencies and color negatives, are viewed and photographed by transmitted light.

Scaling and Cropping

Many different original art elements may be used in producing a printed piece. Some may have to be reduced or enlarged in size, which requires *scaling* and *cropping.* Scaling has to do with changing the size of the original without changing the ratio of the dimensions *(see illustration)*. In addition to the diagonal

DIAGONAL LINE METHOD OF SCALING

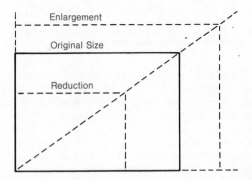

line method of reproduction size, a printer's proportion scale can easily determine a reproduction size. Cropping is a term meaning to eliminate certain areas from the picture.

Assembling Art and Copy

The mechanical is the final assembly of art and copy elements into a unit for photomechanical reproduction. This includes all art and copy, except for full color reproduction which is handled separately. The mechanical is prepared on a white board with all the line copy pasted in position, and with trim, folds and bleeds indicated. The bleed extends past the margin and beyond the trim. It is usually 1/8″. The space allotted for halftones is drawn with a black keyline or blocked out with a red acetate-backed material. This creates a window in the line negative and is photo converted with the line copy.

In preparing art for the camera, line images must be separated from continuous-tone images. Photographically they belong to different groups. Images for full-color reproduction form a third group. Images that are not assembled together must be cross-referenced for easy identification. This operation

MECHANICAL, SHOWING POSITION OF ART AND COPY

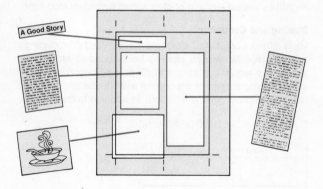

is called *keying*. This can be done by making an outline drawing of the image on the mechanical or by photostats which are pasted where key images will appear. Images keyed for color may be indicated by different colored areas drawn on a tissue overlay on the mechanical.

Both line and continuous-tone elements generally appear on the same board. However, sometimes one is pasted in position on the board and the other on a transparent overlay sheet hinged to the board.

Traditionally, letterpress printing has been from metallic type and photoengravings assembled by skilled craftsmen rather than mechanicals prepared by artists. Layouts consisted of type and engraver's proofs, usually pasted together in position. However, with the advent of photopolymer and wraparound plates, assembly techniques are the same as those used by other printing processes such as offset lithography, for which art and copy is prepared *ready-for-camera*.

Gravure requires extensive assembly of art and copy as each element must be handled separately. Each method of cylinder preparation requires a different handling of the copy. As a rule, type images are not exposed to the gravure tissue with continuous-tone images.

Screen printing art and copy can be prepared either manually with the knife-cut film method, photomechanically, or by a combination of both these methods.

graphic arts
photography

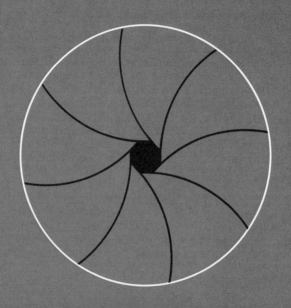

To the printer, there are two types of photography: *creative* and *graphic arts.* Creative photography provides original images for reproduction and is a product of commercial or industrial photographers, art studios, and creative art departments in printing companies. Graphic arts photography is used in the reproduction of art and copy, and is an integral part of the printing process.

GRAPHIC ARTS PHOTOGRAPHY

The materials used in graphic arts photography are similar to those used in creative photography. The usual product of the photographic process is a negative in which the light portions of the copy are represented by heavy or dark deposits of silver, and the dark portions of the copy are light or transparent. When negatives are printed on paper or film they produce positives in which the tone values are similar to what they were on the original copy. Some platemaking processes require negatives, others require positives. Negatives or positives can be line, continuous-tone or halftone, straight reading or reverse reading on the emulsion side.

Light-sensitive photographic materials consist of: (1) a base which may be paper, plastic film or glass, and (2) a light-sensitive coating known as *photographic emulsion,* which is composed essentially of silver salts (halides) in gelatin.

Continuous-tone vs. Halftone

Any picture, photograph, or scene consisting of a broad range of tones or gradation of tones is known as *continuous-tone.* In creative photography these different tones are represented by varying amounts of silver. This metallic silver appears black in the photographic emulsion; it does not look at all like silver. The more silver the darker the image and vice versa.

In letterpress and offset lithography, tones cannot be reproduced by varying the amounts of ink. A press can print only a solid of a color in the image areas, while no ink prints in the non-image areas. In order to reproduce pictures in varying tones, graphic arts photography uses a halftone screen. Halftone photography makes the printing of continuous-tone photographs possible by converting the continuous-tone image into a pattern of very small and clearly defined *dots* of varying sizes. The *halftone principle* is an optical illusion in which tones are represented by a large number of small dots of different sizes printed with ink of uniform film thickness (density) *(see illustration, page 67).*

Some printing processes are capable of printing varying ink densities to produce pictures having a wide range of tones without the need for halftones. Conventional gravure is one. Even though a screen is used, all wells are the same shape and size but they vary in depth so different amounts of ink are printed according to the tone values to be printed. Another process is collotype in which the image consists of reticulated gelatin which prints ink density in proportion to the amount of exposure the gelatin has received through a continuous-tone negative. Screenless lithography has also been used in which the plates are made lithographically from continuous-tone negatives or positives.

Graphic Arts Cameras

A graphic arts camera consists of: copyboard, lensboard, lens, bellows, camera back, and independent camera bed or suspension. The copyboard serves to position the original copy. Many have transparency holders so they can accommodate both reflection and transmission copy. Cameras are traditionally divided into two types, *gallery* and *darkroom*.

Gallery cameras, which are seldom used now, are independent of the darkroom and are located in the camera area. Darkroom cameras are partly in the darkroom and partly in the camera area. Their front ends, consisting of bellows, lens and copyboard, are in the camera area; the camera back or image plane is built into a wall of the darkroom. Darkroom cameras can be operated much more efficiently than gallery cameras because the film is loaded and unloaded in the darkroom.

FLOOR-TYPE HORIZONTAL CAMERA

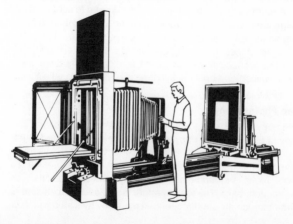

Cameras can be further subdivided into horizontal or vertical types. Horizontal cameras can have either floor-type or overhead suspension. In overhead units, the components are suspended from one or more beams which are, in turn, supported by tall uprights from the floor. The suspension systems are designed to eliminate effects of vibration on the images, as long exposures are used in comparison to creative photography.

Vertical cameras save space. Enlargers, a form of vertical camera, are playing an increasing role in camera departments. They are used mainly for making color separations for color reproduction, especially in the direct screen process.

Lenses are coated and usually of symmetrical design to eliminate distortion in the images. High resolution and minimum aberrations are essential. Therefore lenses have fairly small maximum apertures, ranging from f/8 to f/11. (Note: The larger the f/no. the smaller the lens opening and the longer the exposure.) Focal lengths range from 8" for wide angle lenses for 20" cameras (20" square images), to as long as 48" for a 40" camera. (A 35mm camera has a 2" focal length lens.)

Film Stable base films are used where dimensional stability is critical: for example, color separation photography. Special high contrast emulsions of silver halides in gelatin are used for line and halftone photography. Continuous-tone film is used for color separations and masks. Films are color sensitized. Ordinary or color-blind film is sensitive to ultraviolet (UV) and blue light. Orthochromatic film is sensitive to UV, blue and green light. Panchromatic film is sensitive to UV, blue, green and red light (see illustration).

After developing, the silver halides exposed to light from the image are converted to metallic silver. An important trend in recent years has been the increased use of automatic film processing machines. These processors not only save considerable time but produce more consistent results. Film is developed, fixed, washed and dried in less time than it used to take to just develop it.

Line Photography

Line copy consists of solids, lines, figures, and text matter. The copy is placed on the copyboard, and the film is placed in the vacuum back of the camera. The correct size is focused by adjusting the bellows extension and copyboard extension. To check focus, a ground glass is placed in the same position as the vacuum back. The lens aperture is set, and an exposure is made through the shutter operated manually by a stop watch or

COMPARISON OF COLOR SENSITIVITY
OF EYE AND PHOTOGRAPHIC FILMS

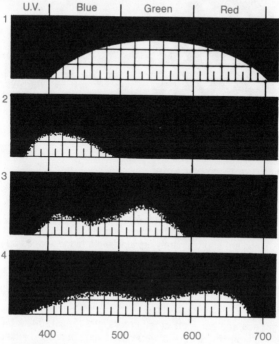

1. Sensitivity of the human eye
2. Ordinary color blind film
3. Orthochromatic film
4. Panchromatic film

automatically by a timer or light integrator. The copy is illuminated by high intensity lights. Usually an orthochromatic film is used. Processing the film produces a negative.

Contact printing Some processes require *contact* negatives or positives. These are made by placing a negative or positive over an unexposed piece of film (usually color blind) in a vacuum frame, then exposing it to a light source. The resulting contact print will be a positive if made from a negative, or a negative if made from a positive. However, it is possible to make negatives from negatives or positives from positives by using special duplicating film, or reversal development, which is seldom used.

ENLARGED GLASS SCREEN   ENLARGED CONTACT SCREEN

HALFTONE PHOTOGRAPHY

Halftone photography is done through the grid pattern of a halftone screen. There are two types of screens: *glass* and *contact*. A glass screen consists of two sheets of glass, each ruled by precision equipment with a given number of lines per linear inch. Lines are approximately equal in width to the spaces between them. The two sheets of glass are cemented together at right angles to each other. The number of lines per inch is designated as the screen ruling. Common screen rulings are: 65- to 85-line for newspapers by letterpress, 100-, 120- and 133-line for offset newspapers, 120-, 133- and 150-line for magazines and commercial letterpress, 133- and 150-line for offset lithography. Special effects have been obtained in offset lithography with 200-line to 300-line screens.

A contact screen is on a film base and is made from a glass screen. Dots are vignetted with variable density across each dot. Density is greatest at the center and lightest at the perimeter. There are gray screens with dots consisting of silver images formed after the film has been exposed, developed and fixed. Dyed screens, usually magenta, contain dots formed by a dye rather than by silver particles. There are also square and elliptical dot screens for special effects, especially in the middletones and Respi screens for special effects in the highlights.

Glass Screen Photography

Photography with a glass screen is accomplished by placing the screen a short distance in front of the film in the back of the camera. During exposure, the light reflected or transmitted from the copy is projected through the transparent spaces of the screen, which act as pinhole lenses to produce dots on the film proportional in size to the amount of light reflected from the copy. The light or *highlight* areas of the copy reflect a lot of light and produce large dots on the negative. The dark or *shadow* areas on the copy reflect little light and the dots are small. The dot sizes in between are produced by the *middletones.*

Screen distance, lens aperture, and length of exposure affect contrast and tone reproduction with the glass screen and are, consequently, very critical factors in halftone photography.

MAKING A HALFTONE NEGATIVE

Film

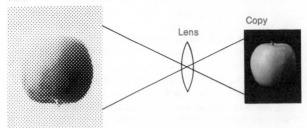

Screen (not shown) can be either crossline glass or contact.

Contact Screen Photography

Photography with a contact screen is much simpler than with a glass screen. The screen is used in direct contact with the film. The variable density of the vignetted dot records variations as larger or smaller dots on the film, depending upon the amount of light reflected or transmitted from the copy. Contrast of reproduction can be varied within limits by techniques known as *flashing* and *no-screen exposure.* Flash exposures are used to reduce contrast especially in the shadows by producing a dot over the whole film and are made by exposing the film to a yellow bulb or light. The no-screen exposure is used for increasing the contrast in the highlights and is done by removing the screen during a short part of the exposure. Additional control of contrast may be achieved with dyed screens by using colored filters during part of the exposure.

Autoscreen halftones Kodak Autoscreen ortho film has a 133-line screen pattern pre-exposed in the film so that when it is used properly in an ordinary camera, a 133-line halftone negative is produced directly without the use of a screen. Two exposures are necessary: (1) a detail exposure to the copy, and (2) a flash exposure with a flash lamp all over the film. The detail exposure produces different size dots according to the amount of light reflected from the copy. The flash exposure is to insure that the inertia of the film is overcome and a dot is produced all over so that there will be adequate detail in the shadows. Autoscreen film uses shorter exposures than glass or contact screens and is capable of higher resolution, especially of type images.

Screened prints There are two methods used for producing screened prints directly in a camera. One is to use Kodak PMT Negative paper with a contact screen. After exposure in the camera the PMT Negative paper is placed in contact with a Kodak PMT Receiver paper and processed in a special diffusion transfer processor. The product is a screened print in the screen ruling of the contact screen used.

Another method is to use the Polaroid MP-3 Copy Camera System. This system comes with a selection of four screens, a special aperture control, and a high contrast print film which produces 4x5 inch screened prints directly in 15 seconds.

Screened prints are useful for pasting up with other copy to make a complete mechanical layout that can be photographed as a line shot in the camera, thus eliminating the need for stripping the halftone negatives. This technique is used for printing newspapers, house organs, school annuals, and other types of work where quality is not critical.

Contrast and Tone Reproduction

Using a stepped gray scale, good tone reproduction results when the darkest area of the subject prints on the press as a solid and the lightest area prints with no evidence of a screen. The films may have very small unprintable dots in these areas which close up in the shadows and disappear in the highlights during printing. Intermediate tones have varying sizes of dots ranging from about 5% in the highlight area to about 90% in the shadows. Some smooth printing plates can print dots as fine as 2-3% in the highlights and 95% in the shadows, on smooth coated paper and under good conditions of printing.

High contrast exists when two or three steps in the shadow end print solid and several steps in the highlight end are white with a corresponding increase in density difference between other steps of the scale.

Low contrast exists when solids contain 80% to 90% dots in the shadows and a 10% to 20% dot in the highlights with corresponding decrease in density difference between other steps in the scale. A number of special techniques may be used to change the contrast in local areas of the reproduction.

COLOR REPRODUCTION

Color reproduction is based on the theory of three-color vision. White light, which contains the wave lengths of all light, is considered to have three primary colors, blue, green, and red. This is the psychological concept of color as distinguished from the physical one in which each wave length of light varies in color from every other. The eye contains three different types of receptors, each sensitive to one of the primary colors of light. When the eye views a color scene, the receptors are activated by the colors to which they are sensitive and impulses are sent to the brain. The brain recreates the scene from the transmitted impulses. The fidelity of the scene is dependent upon the experience of the viewer and the condition of the receptors. If any are diseased or sensitivity is impaired, color blindness results, visual impression is distorted.

The three colors, blue, green and red, are called *additive primaries* because three lights of these colors when added together produce white light.

Color Separation

The process of color separation is analogous to the process of seeing by the eye, but the printing process introduces new concepts. The original is photographed using three filters, each corresponding in color and light transmission to one of the additive primaries.

Placing a red filter over the lens produces a negative recording of all the red light reflected or transmitted from the subject. This is known as the red separation negative. When a positive is made from this negative, the silver in the film will correspond to areas which did *not* contain red but contained the other two colors of light, which are blue and green. In effect, the negative has subtracted the red light from the scene and the positive is a recording of the blue and green in the scene which is called *cyan*. The positive is called the *cyan printer*.

Photography through the green filter produces a negative recording of the green in the original. The positive is a recording of the other additive primaries, red and blue, which is called *magenta*. The positive is called the *magenta printer*.

The blue filter produces a negative which records all the blue in the subject. The positive records the red and green which when combined as additive colors produce *yellow*. This positive is the *yellow printer*.

These three colors, cyan, magenta, and yellow are called *subtractive primaries* because each represents two additive primaries left after one primary has been subtracted from white light. These are the colors of the process inks for process color reproduction.

When the three positives are combined and printed, the result should be a faithful reproduction of the original. Unfortunately, it is not. The colors, outside of yellow and red, are dirty and muddied. There is too much yellow in the reds and greens and too much red in the blues and purples. This is not a flaw in the theory but is due to deficiencies in the colors of the pigments used in the inks.

Corrections must be made in the color separation negatives and positives to overcome the limitations in the colors of the inks. Even after these corrections are made, the printed result would still not be satisfactory. Grays and deep shadows appear brownish.

A fourth, *black printer,* is added to overcome this. It makes the grays and deep shadows neutral and it may be a skeleton or a full black. Most offset lithography is done with the former, while letterpress, especially if it is high speed magazine printing, is done with the latter. Other colors are reduced proportionately so that inks transfer or *trap* properly on high speed presses. This operation of reducing colors and printing a full black in shadow areas is called *undercolor removal.*

Color Correction

Corrections to compensate for the spectral errors in inks may be done manually, photographically or electronically.

Dot etching When done manually, corrections are made in halftone positives by reducing the size of the dots with chemical reducers. This is called *dot etching.* Dots in metal halftone plates for letterpress or gravure may be etched locally after the plates have been made. This is called *fine etching* or *re-etching.*

Masking When color corrections are done photographically, the operation is called *masking.* Numerous methods are used. One way is known as *positive masking.* Each mask is made from one of the separation negatives and placed over another separation negative to correct for the color errors in the different sets of full-color inks. The masks subtract color from the separation negatives in proportion to the strengths of the masks. A simpler masking method uses color-masking materials made up of separate emulsion layers in a single film such as Kodak's Tri-Mask and Gevaert's Multi-mask. Only one mask is used which is made from the original and placed in contact with it in making the color separations.

Direct screening is the simplest method of color separation and correction which produces color corrected halftone separations directly. This method can be used by contact or projection for transparency copy and by projection for reflection copy. Four masks are made—one for each of the four printers, yellow, magenta, cyan and black, or single masks are made on Kodak Tri-mask or Gevaert Multi-mask film. The individual masks for each separation are preferred. In contact and projection printing of transparencies, the masks are registered to the transparency and the color and tone corrected screen separation is made using a gray contact screen and special halftone film. For reflection copy, different masks are used and the mask is placed over the screen in the back of the camera (whence the term *camera back masking*). Special targets are used that have three aim points in the highlight, middletone and shadow ends of the scale to ensure proper tone reproduction in the halftone separations. This system is so simple and popular that a number of special enlargers and exposure computers have been developed for its use.

Electronic scanning can be used to produce the equivalent of color correction by photographic masking. A light beam scanning the original is split into three beams. Each beam goes to a photocell covered with a filter that corresponds to one of the additive primaries, thus separating each area of the copy into its three color components *(see illustration)*. Electrical currents

PRINCIPLE OF AN ELECTRONIC SCANNER

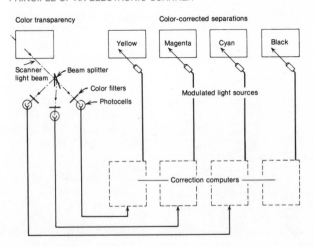

from the photocell are fed into four separate computers, one for each color and one for the black which is computed from the other three signals. The computers can be reset to modify currents depending on the inks, paper, tonal range and other printing conditions. The modified currents are fed to exposing lights which vary in intensity in proportion to the corrected value of each element in the area scanned as they expose the corrected color separations on film. Some scanners produce one color-corrected separation at a time. Older scanners produce continuous-tone negative or positive color separation film which must be converted to halftone by conventional photographic methods. Newer scanners use analog to digital converters to enlarge or reduce the image and contact screens or lasers to produce halftone images directly.

Screen Angles

In multicolor printing there is a problem which is not usually present in black-and-white halftone or in screenless printing. This is the danger of producing an undesirable *moiré* (pronounced moa-wray) pattern when multicolor halftone images are not properly printed. The print will show a pattern that interferes with its appearance.

By proper angling of halftone screens moiré patterns can be avoided. A minimum pattern is formed when an angle of 30° between screens is used. Since halftone screens consist of line rulings at 90° to each other, there is room for only three 30° angles before they repeat. In four-color printing, two of the colors must be printed at the same angle or must be separated by other than 30°. As a rule, because yellow is a light color, it is printed at an angle of 15° from two other colors, generally cyan and magenta. Usual screen angles are: black, 45°; magenta, 75°; yellow, 90°; and cyan, 105° *(see illustration, page 96).*

MOIRÉ PATTERNS

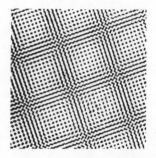

An error as small as 0.1° between screen angles or a slight misregister between colors can cause moiré in areas where three and four colors print.

A moiré pattern can also be caused by improper transfer of ink, a condition called *poor trapping*. Proper trapping is when the same amount of ink transfers to both the previously printed and unprinted areas of the paper. If inks are not formulated to trap properly, the results will show up as weak overprint colors (red, blue and green) and accentuated moiré patterns.

Pre-Separated Color Printing (fake color process)

In this type of color printing, the original is usually a black-and-white photograph or a black-and-white wash drawing. This process obviously is much less expensive to reproduce than four-color process.

Various areas of the original are translated into colors which are reproduced with process inks. Usually the design studio will specify the desired colors by indicating halftone percentages for different areas of the reproduction; sometimes the printer or photoengraver will use trained specialists for this type of work. A number of color charts are available to be used as guides to determine approximate dot percentages for required colors.

RETOUCHING AND OPAQUING

After negatives or positives have been made, the individual films must be prepared before they are ready to make plates. For conventional gravure, the continuous-tone negatives and positives are retouched so that they have the proper tone values for printing. These operations are done by the retoucher. For halftone gravure, letterpress and lithography, and for line drawings and text, the negatives or positives are trimmed, marked for register or cutting, and opaqued.

Camera negatives of line copy, such as type or line drawings, contain pinholes and other flaws. These are eliminated with an application of a special preparation called *opaque,* which when applied to pinholes and other flaws in the film, makes them opaque to light so they do not print when a contact print or plate is made from the film. The operation is usually called *spotting* and is done on a light table. The opaquer or stripper also does squaring and outlining of halftones as well as contacting several film elements to produce a final composite image on film. He may, in finishing, add *register marks* and *trim marks.* Register marks indicate the correct fit for successive printed images; trim marks are guides for folding and trimming the printed sheet.

PIN REGISTER SYSTEMS

In addition to register marks, films are most commonly registered now by the use of pin register systems. These systems consist of punching two or three holes or slots in films and copy, and placing pins which fit in the holes or slots so the copy or several pieces of film can be held in place during exposure and will assure exposure or placement in the correct position. They assure register when pieces of film are removed and replaced. Pin bars in which pins are spaced at the same distance as the holes in the film are used for making multiple exposures on films or plates. Pin register devices are an important part of color separation systems and are often used starting with the copy and continuing through to the press.

The following 12 pages illustrate many photomechanical treatments in both black-and-white and color. Included are various types and screenings of halftones, special line screens, the principle of four-color process printing, and color process charts.

The text is continued on page 98.

GRADATION AND MAGNIFICATION OF TONES

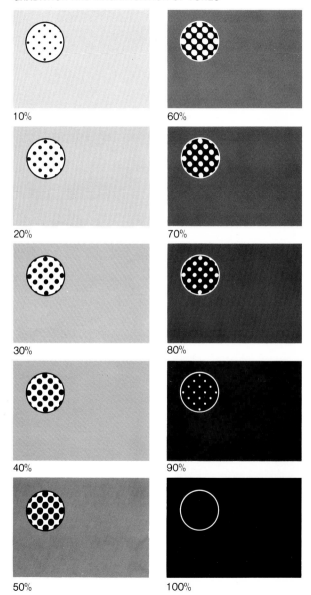

10%

20%

30%

40%

50%

60%

70%

80%

90%

100%

HALFTONE SCREENS

65 LINE SCREEN

100 LINE SCREEN

150 LINE SCREEN

TYPES OF HALFTONES

HIGH CONTRAST HALFTONE

VIGNETTE HALFTONE

OUTLINE HALFTONE

SPECIAL LINE SCREENS

STRAIGHT LINE

MEZZO TINT

ETCH TONE

DRY BRUSH

RANDOM LINE

TWO COLOR TEXTURE

DUOTONES

STANDARD DUOTONE

DUOTONE EFFECT

TINTS AND TYPE

White Type Dropout Black Type Overprint	White Type Dropout Black Type Overprint	White Type Dropout Black Type Overprint
50% COLOR	30% COLOR	10% COLOR

BLACK HALFTONE OVER COLOR

White Type Dropout Black Type Overprint	White Type Dropout Black Type Overprint	White Type Dropout Black Type Overprint
50% COLOR	30% COLOR	10% COLOR

BLACK HALFTONE OVER COLOR

50% BLACK	30% BLACK	10% BLACK

FOUR COLOR PROCESS PRINTING

BLUE FILTER / YELLOW PRINTER

GREEN FILTER / MAGENTA PRINTER

RED FILTER / CYAN PRINTER

MODIFIED FILTER / BLACK PRINTER

ROTATION OF COLORS

YELLOW

YELLOW & MAGENTA

YELLOW, MAGENTA & CYAN

YELLOW, MAGENTA, CYAN & BLACK

TWO COLOR PROCESS CHARTS

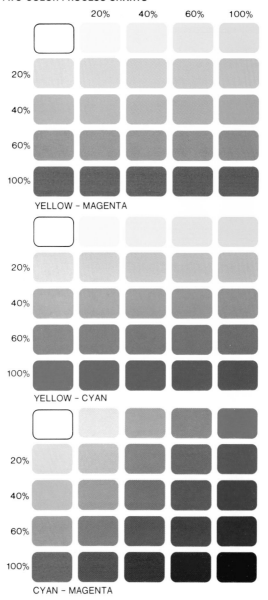

YELLOW – MAGENTA

YELLOW – CYAN

CYAN – MAGENTA

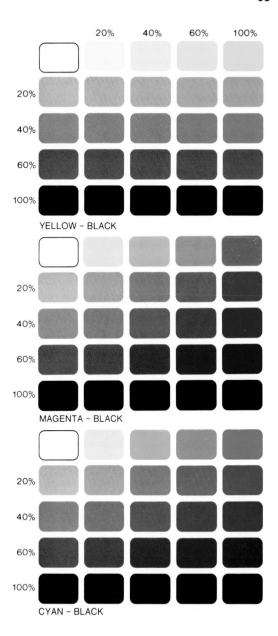

YELLOW – BLACK

MAGENTA – BLACK

CYAN – BLACK

FOUR COLOR PROCESS MAGNIFIED DOT PATTERN

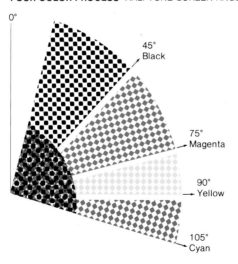

FOUR COLOR PROCESS HALFTONE SCREEN ANGLES

0°

45°
Black

75°
Magenta

90°
Yellow

105°
Cyan

stripping
and
imposition

The terms *stripping* and *imposition* are essentially synonymous as they both refer to the planned assembly of images for printing. The term imposition originated in letterpress and since this is the oldest of the printing processes, the term is still used although it is replaced in photomechanical processes like lithography and gravure, by the term stripping. The important fact to be stressed is that both imposition and stripping depend on a plan for the assembly of the images for printing. In the photomechanical processes, the plan is often referred to as a press layout (not to be confused with an *art* layout), while the term imposition is still used in letterpress.

This layout, or imposition, is needed at the planning stage when a number of pages are to be printed in the same form. Otherwise when the sheet is printed, folded and trimmed, the pages will not appear in the proper sequence. Some presses, of course, print single pages and some print multiples of the same subjects such as in labels and packaging. In any case, all material for printing must be planned to appear in the proper order in the final printed piece.

STRIPPING

For photomechanical platemaking such as used for lithography, gravure, wraparound letterpress, letterset, and photopolymer plates, the negatives representing the printing images or pages are taped in position on a sheet of plastic or colored paper called *goldenrod*. This assembly of the negatives in position is called a *flat*. When all film is in place, the stripper cuts windowed spaces from the goldenrod or plastic, permitting light to pass through the image areas during exposure to the plate.

Layouts or imposition will vary among printers, because of variations in the size of printing and binding equipment. For special jobs, the layout should be prepared by, or checked with, the bindery to make sure it can be processed in the folding or other finishing equipment. However, certain basic rules are followed. After page size has been determined, 1/8″ to 1/4″ is added on the top, side and bottom for trim. If the page numbers or folios are not already on the film they are inserted at this point and, on larger signatures, the center or gutter margin is varied according to the position of the page in the signature and the bulk of the paper.

The stripper checks all negatives carefully for opaquing, dimensions, register and cut marks, position and layout. He also puts together all elements on a page if they are in separate pieces. If positives are needed for deep-etch, some bi-metal plates, and gravure cylinders, contact exposures on film are made of the individual negatives or stripped up flats depending on the particular use or application.

There are three basic types of arrangement of pages for printing: (1) sheetwise; (2) work-and-turn; and (3) work-and-tumble. In sheetwise layouts, different pages are printed on each side of the sheet. It is used when the number of pages to be printed is large enough to fill the full capacity of the press.

In both work-and-turn and work-and-tumble layouts, the front and back of the pages are printed on the same form, and there are two finished units to the sheet. Once printed, the sheet is cut in half for folding. In work-and-turn, after the first side is printed, the sheet is turned over from left to right for the printing of the second side. The same gripper edge is used for printing both sides. In work-and-tumble, after the first side is printed, the sheet is turned over from gripper edge to back for the printing of the second side. However, changing the gripper edge can cause problems in register unless the paper is accurately squared and trimmed before printing.

Books and magazines are printed in units of several pages per sheet called *signatures*. There may be from 2 to 64 pages on each side of the sheet, depending on the size of the page and how large a form the press can print.

Projection stripping The latest development in stripping is the use of special projectors in which the images are reduced – one-half to one-eighth in size (2X-8X) – on negatives, programming the individual images and projecting them back to correct size on the plate in the proper order and correct position for printing. With such systems, stripping of repetitive layouts as in book printing, can be speeded up and appreciable savings in the cost of film can be made. At 1/3 reduction the saving in film is about 67%, and at 1/8 reduction the saving is 88%.

At the 1/8th reduction there is little loss in the quality of line or text images. Highlight and shadow dots in fine screen halftones, however, are lost, so the system is only useful at present for line work or for reductions not exceeding 1/4 (4X) when the copy contains halftones.

Reprojection of the images poses several other problems. There are presently two systems of projection in use. (1) Use of quartz optics, which transmit UV light, and exposure onto diazo sensitized plates. This is expensive, as quartz optics are scarce. (2) Use of regular optical systems and projecting the image onto film or special plates like Kodak Verilith which is used in the Addressograph-Multigraph Photo Direct, Itek Platemaster and A.B. Dick Photomat processes, but are not available in large sizes nor have the plate life or quality of conventional lithographic plates. The new diffusion transfer processes like the Kodak PMT *(see page 118)* offer some promise.

IMPOSITION (for letterpress)

In letterpress, the pages or image elements must be combined as in stripping, but it is done with metal type and photoengraved illustrations instead of film. As in offset, an imposition layout or diagram is first made showing how a given number of pages must be arranged to produce the proper result after folding. For printing on a flat-bed press, the metal type and photoengraved images are assembled into page form, arranged in proper position on an imposing stone, and locked up in a chase that is mounted on the bed of a press. An optical pre-register device is sometimes used in lockup which is more accurate and saves time. For printing on a rotary press, curved electrotypes or stereotypes are mounted on the cylinder of a press in proper position.

The layouts shown illustrate the most common impositions for 4, 6, 8, 12, and 16 page forms. The letters A, B, and C indicate the folding sequence.

FOUR PAGE FOLDER

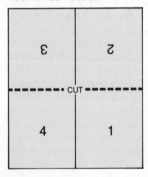

SIX PAGE FOLDER

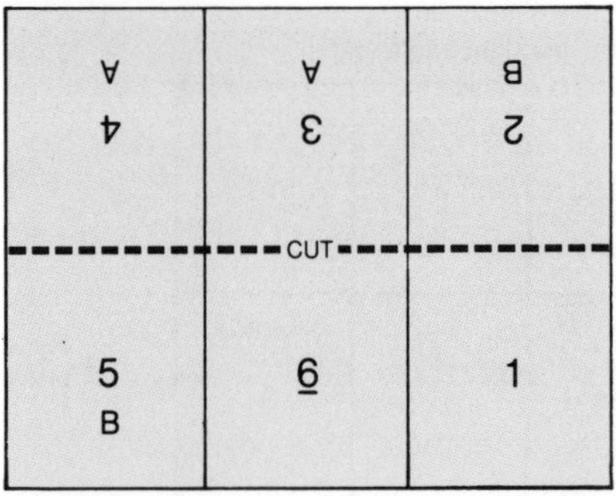

EIGHT PAGE FORM
Work and Turn
one parallel, one right angle fold

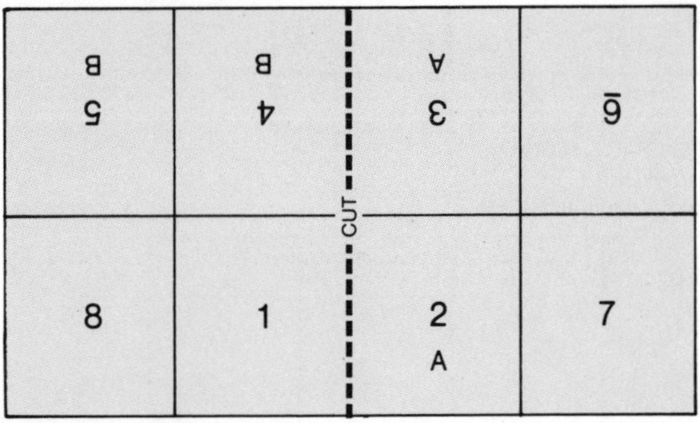

EIGHT PAGE FORM
Work and Tumble
two parallel folds

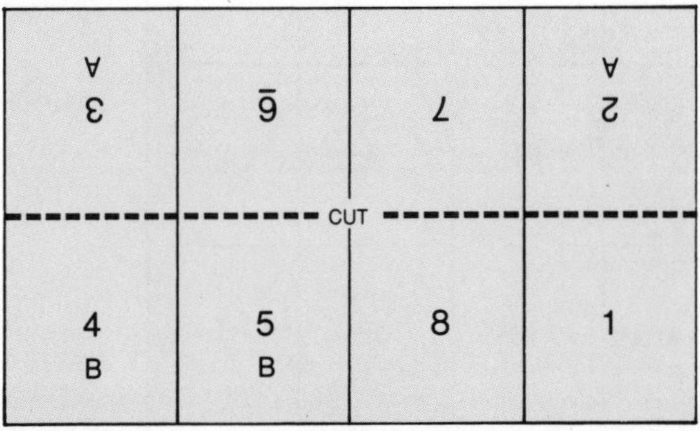

TWELVE PAGE FORM
Work and Turn
two parallel (accordion), one right angle fold

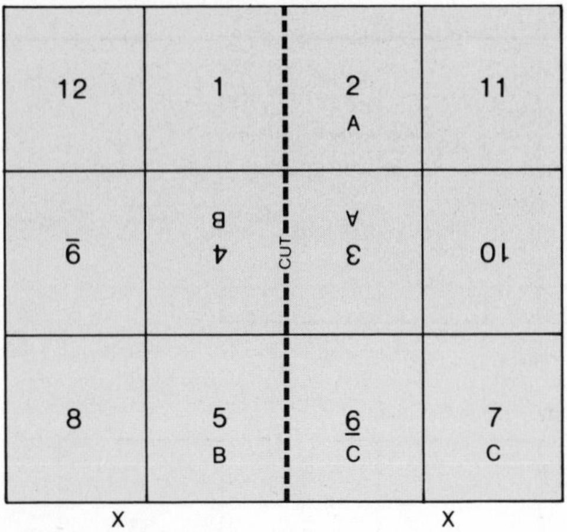
12
1
2
A
11
9_
B
4
CUT
A
3
10
8
5
B
6_
C
7
C
X
X

SIXTEEN PAGE FORM
Work and Turn
three right angle folds

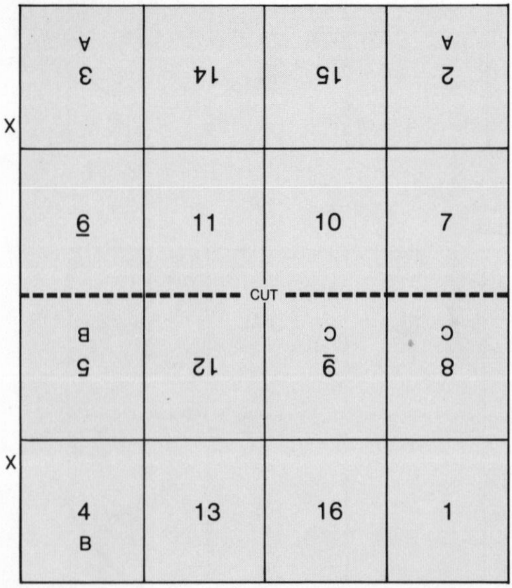
A
3
14
15
A
2
X
6_
11
10
7
CUT
B
5
12
C
9_
C
8
X
4
B
13
16
1

platemaking

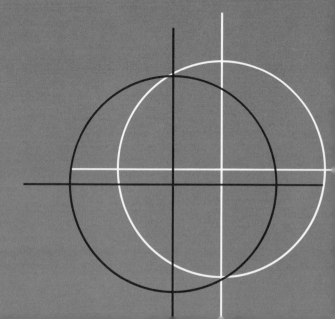

An important part of all printing processes is the making of the intermediate image carrier or plate, which is used for printing the multiple copies on the press. As would be expected, each printing process uses a different kind of image carrier. These image carriers or plates vary in cost and determine the characteristics of the image produced, the type of ink and press to be used, the number of impressions that can be printed, and the speed with which they are printed.

Appearance differences of the final printed images are not as noticeable as they were years ago. Lithography, letterpress and gravure are all capable of reproducing the same art and copy with equally satisfactory results. There are still some distinguishing characteristics, but these are minor. Factors such as economics, availability of equipment, and speed of delivery are now the main considerations in selecting a printing process, rather than quality or appearance of the image.

METHODS OF PRODUCING PRINTING IMAGE CARRIERS

Image carriers can be made in a number of ways depending on the printing process, length of run, type of press, etc.

Manual image carriers consist of hand-set composition, woodcuts, linoleum blocks, copperplate or steel-die engravings, all produced manually, as was done for hundreds of years after the invention of movable type. These are seldom used now except for short runs and unusual effects. Manually made images are still used commercially in screen printing and manually drawn images on stone are used by artists to produce original or limited editions of lithographs.

Mechanical image carriers are produced mostly for relief printing. They fall into two categories: (1) hot-metal machine composition and (2) duplicate printing plates. Hot-metal machine composition is formed by casting molten metal in molds and type matrices *(see page 49)*. In duplicate platemaking, each of the many different kinds is arrived at by a different production method and with different materials. Electrotypes, although made by electrolysis, require molding, casting, finishing and machining; stereotypes require casting and machining; rubber and plastic plates require molding of thermosetting and thermoplastic materials as well as finishing of the molded plates.

Intaglio printing also uses mechanically made plates such as pantograph engravings and engravings made with geometric lathes. Pantograph engravings are used in steel-die engraving. Geometric lathes produce scrolls and other patterns that are used for stock and bond certificates and national paper currency. Mechanically made gravure cylinders are also used for the printing of textiles, wrapping papers, wallpapers and plastics.

Photomechanical platemaking is the most important and universally used method of platemaking. It makes use of light-sensitive coatings on which images are produced photographically and processed according to the requirements of the printing method used *(see Photomechanics, below)*. Photomechanics overcomes the limitations of manually and mechanically produced plates and is capable of reproducing photographs and other pictorial subjects. Photomechanical plates used for letterpress are made by the photoengraving process. Photomechanical lithographic plates can be surface, deep-etch or bi-metal, depending primarily upon the length of run. For intaglio printing, photomechanics produces either gravure plates or cylinders. Photomechanics also produces the photographic screens used in screen printing.

Electronic equipment has been developed to convert original images directly into relief printing plates. These are used primarily for low-cost picture reproduction and are practical for letterpress printing of newspapers. They are also used for producing engraved color separations on plastic. Electronic engraving machines are now in use for automatically engraving gravure cylinders. Positives or negatives of the copy made on a special opaque white plastic are scanned as the cylinder is being engraved electromechanically by special diamond styli. Developments are underway to (1) reproduce directly from full color copy and (2) use electron-beam or laser etching to speed up the process.

Electrostatic plates are not generally used in commercial printing, although *Xerography* has proven to be an economical method of producing lithographic plates. These plates are very popular in the reprography and office-duplicating field. *Electrofax* cameras convert original images directly into a final image carrier for lithography and are used for producing plates for copier/duplicators *(see page 36)*.

PHOTOMECHANICS

The light-sensitive coatings used in the photomechanical process change in physical properties after exposure to light. The exposed areas of the coating harden, becoming insoluble in water or other solutions. The unexposed areas dissolve, leaving the exposed portion as an image, or a stencil to form an image.

Originally, natural organic substances such as asphalt and

shellac and natural organic colloids like albumin and gum arabic were used as ingredients for photomechanical coatings. Chemistry has introduced new materials such as polyvinyl alcohol, diazo compounds, photopolymers, etc. Until 1950, when diazo presensitized plates were introduced, practically all coatings used for photomechanical plates were bichromated colloids. Some are still in use.

Bichromated coatings still in use consist of bichromated gelatin for gravure carbon tissue and collotype, and bichromated gum arabic for deep-etch and bimetal plates. The coatings are usually applied to metal plates in a *whirler* which spreads the coating over a whirling plate by centrifugal force. Use of bichromated colloids requires considerable skill and judgment. Sensitivity is affected by a number of factors such as temperature, relative humidity, pH (acidity) and coating thickness which, itself, is affected by surface roughness, relative humidity, rate of application of coating, coating temperature and viscosity. The difficulty of controlling these factors has helped promote the use of presensitized and precoated plates for all processes.

Diazo coatings are used basically for presensitized and wipe-on lithographic plates. With wipe-on plates, the coating is wiped on with a sponge or applied with a roller coater. Plates may have either a relatively smooth or finely grained surface which has been pretreated with a silicate or anodized to accept the coating and to prevent a reaction with the metal. Diazo coatings are thin and are used for plates having press runs under 75,000 impressions. Some prelacquered plates are capable of runs over 200,000 impressions. Most diazo coatings are used for negative plates, but coatings are sometimes used to presensitize positive plates, deep-etch and bimetal plates. The main advantage of diazo coatings is that they are not affected appreciably under normal conditions by temperature and relative humidity. Temperatures above 125°F can cause scumming of plates. Storage life for presensitized plates is about a year.

Photopolymer coatings is a generic term for the use of synthetic resins for platemaking. They are usually very inert and abrasion resistant which allows runs longer than those usually obtained with diazo coatings.

Photopolymer plates are always supplied precoated. They are not only resistant to abrasion but also have low sensitivity to changes in temperature and relative humidity. They have long storage life before use, and good wear characteristics in printing. Some have good solvent resistance so they can be used in processes like flexography, that use solvent inks.

Plate Exposure

The photomechanical process is the most extensive for making plates for all three printing processes. It uses light-sensitive coatings which must be exposed to light of certain wavelengths in order for the coatings to behave as they should in the photomechanical process. Two methods for exposure are used: (1) *Vacuum frame* and (2) *Step and repeat.*

Vacuum frame Exposures on plates are made in a vacuum frame if all the negatives are stripped up on a single flat or if the same flat is to be exposed two or more times on a plate, in which case pin register devices can be used to make sure that the exposures are made in the proper position. Sometimes two or more flats are exposed on the same plate. This is known as *surprinting.* This is done with flats consisting of negatives, but is not normally done with positives. When positives are used, all elements are combined on one flat before the exposures are made.

Step and repeat When more than four exposures are to be made on a plate from the same or different subjects, it is usually more economical and accurate to use a step and repeat machine. These are sometimes called *photocomposing* machines, but this terminology is confusing especially with the recent development of phototypesetting which is also called photocomposing at times. Therefore, the term step and repeat is preferred.

STEP AND REPEAT MACHINE

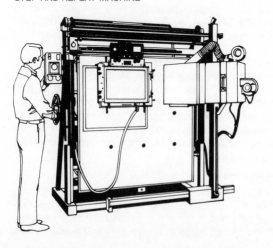

A step and repeat machine is designed to produce multiple images of negatives or positives on a printing plate. It consists of a bed for mounting the plate which is usually held by vacuum during exposure; a chase for mounting the film for exposure; a means for traversing the chase accurately in two directions; and a high intensity lamp like pulsed Xenon or metal halide for exposure. Some step and repeat machines have devices for moving the chase in both directions automatically using programmed punched tape or punched cards. Some are also equipped with film cassettes so that they operate completely automatically by rejecting one film after all the exposures with that film have been completed and picking up the next film for continuing the exposures on the plate. Such machines are very useful in packaging and label printing where a number of exposures of different subjects are made on a plate. The automatic machines are also useful in book production where the negatives are programmed in advance for exposure in the proper position on the plate.

LETTERPRESS PLATES

Plates used for letterpress printing can be *original, direct, duplicate,* or *wraparound.* Original plates are usually photoengravings made on zinc, magnesium or copper of about 16 gauge (0.065″) in thickness. They are called *direct* plates if they are used for printing. Photopolymer plates are usually used as direct plates and some are made for making molds for duplicate plates, especially mats for stereotypes. Duplicate plates are made from original engravings and can be plastic, rubber, stereotypes or electrotypes, depending on the materials used. Most direct and duplicate plates are made in small units or page size for assembly in a form or on the printing cylinder of the press.

Wraparound plates are made in one piece to be wrapped around the plate cylinder of a printing press. All copy is in proper position for printing. Setup or makeready time is substantially reduced. Plates are plastic or metal, ranging from 0.017″ to 0.030″ in thickness so they can be bent to fit into the cylinder clamps. Wraparound plates are also used for dry offset or letterset printing.

Photoengraving

The oldest of all photomechanical processes, photoengraving pertains to the production of relief printing plates for letterpress. Photoengraved plates fall into two categories: *line* and *halftone.* These can be made in a number of combinations, from line or halftone in one color, to combinations of line and halftone in one to four colors. In the U.S., line engravings are made on zinc and magnesium, and halftone plates are made on copper. In Europe, zinc is used for all types of engravings.

Conventional etching The plate is coated with a light-sensitive coating, exposed to a negative and processed according to the coating used. The exposed coating serves as a resist for protecting the image areas as the non-image areas are etched in acid baths. Nitric acid is used for etching zinc and magnesium, and ferric chloride is used for etching copper.

The main problem in etching is to maintain the correct dot and line width at the proper etch depth. This is accomplished in conventional etching by *scale compression* in the negative and *four-way powdering* on the engraving. Etching proceeds in stages known as *bites*. After the first bite, or *flat etch,* the plate is dusted with an acid resistant fusible powder called *dragon's blood,* which after heating and fusing protects the sides of the etched image elements.

The plate is etched a number of times to deepen the area around the relief portions, a powdering and fusing following each etch. Care must be taken to prevent *undercutting* (etching laterally beneath the printing surface). Undercutting weakens the engraving, causing it to break down under pressure in printing. Also, undercut images will stick in the molding material used for electrotypes and stereotypes.

Conventional etching is time consuming and requires considerable skill and judgment. It has been replaced almost completely by powderless etching.

Powderless etching is an important simplification and improvement in the making of photoengravings and can be used for zinc, magnesium, and copper plates. Zinc and magnesium use the same process. Copper uses essentially the same principles, but the chemicals and mechanism are different. The plate is prepared as in the conventional process, but a special etching machine is used. Zinc and magnesium are etched in an emulsion of dilute nitric acid, a wetting agent and an oil. During etching, the wetting agent and oil attach to the surface of the metal forming an etch-resistant coating on the sidewalls of the etched elements, thus preventing undercutting.

In copper etching, the etchant used is ferric chloride, in which certain organic chemicals are dissolved. During etching, the additive chemicals react with the dissolved metal, to form a gelatinous precipitate which adheres to the sides of the image elements and protects them from undercutting.

Photopolymer plates are precoated and can be used as original (or direct) and wraparound plates. There are many in use today, as well as in development. Two examples are: the DuPont *Dycril* and the BASF *Nyloprint* plates. At the present time the Nyloprint plate, on a steel base and mounted on magnetic cylinders, is the most popular plate used in letterpress for magazine and commercial printing.

Two photopolymer plates used extensively in newspaper printing are the W.R. Grace *Letterflex* and the *Dynaflex* plates. Over 200 daily newspapers are using these plates either exclusively or experimentally. The Letterflex plate is also used almost exclusively on the Cameron belt press, which prints complete books in one pass through the press. This eliminates the present practice of printing large signatures which must be folded, stored or stacked, and later collated into the final book.

During the past several years, many new Japanese photopolymer plates have been introduced for direct letterpress printing, as well as a plastic-molded plate. These are used mainly in newspaper printing. Two of them, the NAPP and the Merigraph plates, are now manufactured and used in the U.S.

Duplicate Plates

Original photoengravings can be used directly for printing. Generally, however, the original plates are used to make molds from which duplicate plates are made for the actual printing. This is desirable for long runs and is necessary where the plates are made on flat metal and the printing plates need to be curved for mounting on the cylinders of rotary presses. Also the original and mold are always available in case printing plates are damaged. The four types of duplicate plates in use are *stereotypes, electrotypes, plastic,* and *rubber* plates.

Stereotypes are used almost exclusively for letterpress newspaper printing. A matrix, or *mat* as it is called, is made from the

FOUR STEPS IN MAKING A STEREO

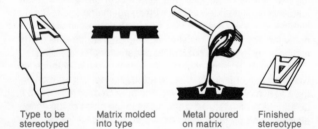

| Type to be stereotyped | Matrix molded into type | Metal poured on matrix | Finished stereotype |

original plate using a special papier-mâché and the printing plate is cast by pouring molten metal into the mold. For long runs the plates can be nickel or chromium plated. Once the mat is made, duplicate plates can be made in less than a minute and at costs under a dollar per square foot. For economical substitution of direct photopolymer plates for newspaper printing they must compete with these time and cost schedules. In newspaper printing the presses are seldom run over two hours in which time about 100,000 newspapers are printed. If more papers are needed, more presses are used.

Electrotypes are used for high quality letterpress, commercial, book and magazine printing. An impression is made of the original engraving in hot plastic which is plated with silver to make it conductive, after which a thin shell of copper or nickel is plated by an electrolytic process. The shell is backed with molten metal and the face can be nickel, chromium or iron plated for long runs up to several million.

Plastic and rubber plates have the advantage of lightness in weight and low cost. They are made from molds similar to those used for electrotypes. Plastic plates are molded from thermoplastic vinyl resins and are used for some types of commercial printing. Rubber plates are molded from either natural or synthetic rubber or combinations of them, depending on the solvents used in the inks for printing. Rubber plates are used exclusively in flexography for printing on rough surfaces such as envelopes, bags, tags, wrapping paper, corrugated boxes, milk cartons, as well as on extensible films for flexible packaging. Paperback books are printed from rubber plates, but the process is letterpress rather than flexography as oil base inks are used instead of the solvent inks used in flexography.

LITHOGRAPHIC PLATES

Lithography is based on the principle that grease and water do not mix. On a lithographic plate the separation between the image and non-image areas is maintained chemically since they are essentially on the same plane; the image area must be ink receptive and refuse water, and the non-image area must be water receptive and refuse ink. In reality, the grease and water do mix slightly. If they didn't, lithography would not be possible. If they mix too much, there are problems. The wider the difference that can be maintained between the ink receptivity of the image areas and the water receptivity of the non-image areas, the better the plate will be, the easier it will run on the press, and consequently, the better printing will be produced.

Ink receptivity is accomplished by using inherently oleophilic (oil-loving) resins or metals like copper or brass on the image areas. Water receptivity of the non-image areas is usually achieved by using hydrophilic (water-loving) metals like aluminum, chromium or stainless steel. Water receptivity is maintained in platemaking and storage by using natural and synthetic gums. The most widely used is gum arabic.

One advantage of lithographic plates, besides low cost, is the ease of making minor corrections on press. However, for extensive corrections a new plate is made. Tone values can be easily controlled with the use of the GATF Sensitivity Guide, Star Target, and Dot Gain Scale.

There are three types of lithographic plates: *surface, deep-etch* and *bimetal.*

Surface Plates

Surface plates are those in which the light-sensitive coating becomes the ink-receptive image area on the plate. Most are made from negatives. There are two types of surface plates, *additive* and *subtractive.* On the additive plate the ink-receptive material is added to the plate during processing. On the subtractive plate the ink-receptive lacquer is already on the plate as part of the precoating, and processing removes it from the non-printing areas. Such plates are often referred to as *prelacquered* plates.

Until recently all surface plates were used for short or medium runs. For many years albumin plates dominated this field but they are now obsolete. Today, surface plates are either diazo presensitized (precoated) or wipe-on (in-plant coated) for short and medium runs, and prelacquered diazo presensitized and photopolymer plates for longer runs.

Diazo presensitized and wipe-on plates are easy to process. Once exposed to a negative, they are treated with an emulsion developer which consists of a lacquer and gum etch in acid solution. As the unexposed diazo is dissolved by the solution, the gum deposits on the non-printing areas insuring water receptivity, and lacquer deposits on the exposed images making them ink receptive. Once developed, the plate is rinsed with water and coated with a protective gum arabic solution. Prelacquered plates are developed with a special solvent, washed and then gummed. On most plates made from positives the image must be stabilized during processing, requiring several extra steps in the procedure. Some newer positive plates of the photopolymer type use very simple processing techniques.

Most surface plates of the photopolymer type are made

AUTOMATIC PLATE PROCESSOR

from negatives. These plates can be processed either by hand or by special automatic processors. The finished printing plates are characterized by better abrasion resistance and longer press runs.

Automatic processors for platemaking are used almost as extensively as for photography. Each plate process or special plate has an automatic processor that can be used for it. These processors have been helpful in the expansion of newspapers into web offset. Some processors combine exposure with the processing, and at least one includes coating as well.

Deep-etch Plates

On deep-etch plates, the coating in the image areas is removed and these are then coppered chemically and/or lacquered and inked so that they are ink receptive. The majority of deep-etch plates are made using grained aluminum plates and a bichromated gum arabic coating. Some deep-etch plates are manufactured presensitized and precoated and some are made on anodized aluminum. Procedures for making deep-etch plates are involved and require considerable skill.

After being cleaned, coated and dried, the plates are exposed to positives. Film edges, unexposed borders and other unexposed areas in the coating in the non-printing areas are covered with a special lacquer.

Plates are developed in a special developer that dissolves the unexposed bichromated gum arabic corresponding to the image areas. It is then treated with a deep-etching solution that dissolves some of the metal in the image areas. The plate is cleaned with anhydrous alcohol and the image areas are chemically copperized with a special solution. After the copper is deposited, it is cleaned again with alcohol, and a thin film of special vinyl lacquer is applied over all the plate and dried.

A liquid greasy ink is also applied and dried after which the plate is soaked in warm water. The gum stencil on the non-image areas softens and is scrubbed off with a bristle brush. Once clear of the gum stencil, a gum etch (desensitizer) is applied after which gum is dried on the plate.

The making of anodized aluminum deep-etch plates is similar, except special chemicals and lacquers are used, and the plates cannot be copperized.

Several deep-etch processes are in use today in which the deep-etching and alcohol washing steps are eliminated. These shorten the processing time appreciably, save on the use of alcohol, and make deep-etch platemaking more competitive with photopolymer plates.

Bimetal Plates

Bimetal plates are similar to deep-etch plates in that the coating is removed from image areas but these areas consist of copper or brass. (Base metal for surface and deep-etch plates is usually aluminum.) There are two types of bimetal plates: (1) copper plated on stainless steel or aluminum and (2) chromium plated on copper or brass. (The copper can be plated on a third metal which becomes the base, as in trimetal plates.) Some bimetal plates are made from negatives and others are made from positives. Bimetal plates are the most rugged and also the most expensive of lithographic plates, but they are capable of runs in excess of a million impressions. The increase in cost is not significant when they are used on long runs. Some of the copper-plated plates are presensitized, although most bimetal plates are presently in-plant coated.

Materials and processing are similar to the deep-etch process. Major differences are (1) an actual metal etch is used in place of the deep-etching step and (2) the copper is sensitized to take ink instead of using lacquer and ink. In copper-plated plates the copper must be dissolved from the non-image areas, whereas in chromium-plated plates the chromium must be dissolved from the image areas.

Bimetal plates are easiest to run on the press because they are almost indestructible. Should anything happen to the plate on press (the copper may refuse to take ink or the non-printing area may scum) a single acid treatment restores the plate to its original condition. With other types of plates, treatments used on press to restore ink-receptive areas often are injurious to water-receptive areas and vice versa.

Driography

Driography is a new printing process which is similar to lithography in that the plates are planographic but they print without water. The process eliminates all of the disadvantages caused by the need for an ink-water balance in lithography but retains all its advantages of low plate costs, ease of makeready, high speed, and good print quality plus the advantages of letterpress of ease of printing and low waste. The process is still in limited use because of the need for special inks.

Diographic plates consist of aluminum coated with diazo sensitizer and a silicone rubber. On exposure and processing, the silicone and diazo are removed in the image areas leaving a plate with ink on metal for the image and silicone rubber for the non-image areas. Silicone rubber has a very low surface energy and thus has the property of not wanting to be wet by anything, especially ink. However, under the pressure of printing, ordinary litho ink has a tendency to smear over the silicone and cause scumming or *toning*. Therefore, a special ink has to be used which has low surface energy or tendency to spread.

Such inks have high cohesive forces which affect their flow characteristics and increase their tack. The high tack has caused some problems with picking on coated papers and linting on newsprint and some uncoated stocks. Also most inks formulated for driography have been unstable and caused toning after several hours' running on the press. There have been several successful runs of up to 90,000 impressions on web presses equipped with water-cooled rollers. The answer to the problem of stabilizing ink and running driographic plates successfully may be as simple as using water-cooled rollers in the ink train on the press.

The process has tremendous potential for use in most printing applications when the problems of ink formulation and stability are resolved.

GRAVURE PLATEMAKING

In *conventional* gravure, the image is transferred to the copper cylinder by the use of a sensitized gelatin transfer medium known as *carbon tissue.* The carbon tissue is first exposed in contact with a gravure screen. (The screen serves a purely mechanical purpose, and, unlike other processes, has nothing to do with producing the *tones* of the picture. It merely provides the partitions or walls of the cells etched into the cylinder to form a surface of uniform height for the doctor blade to ride on.) Then the continuous tone positives are exposed in contact with the carbon tissue.

Where light passes through freely, as in the lightest tones, the gelatin on the carbon tissue becomes proportionately harder than where the light exposure is restrained. The carbon tissue thus has areas of varying hardness due to varying exposure to light. The carbon tissue is positioned on the copper plate or cylinder with precision machines. After removal of a paper backing, the tissue is developed in a tank of hot water, leaving gelatin of various thickness in the square dot areas between the hardened screen lines. The etching is done in stages using solutions of ferric chloride at varying density (Baumé) levels. Photographic resists are being developed to replace the carbon tissue. They are more stable, easier to use and can be stored for a longer period of time.

Conventional gravure is used for high quality black and white and color illustrations but mainly for short runs because of doctor blade wear of the shallow highlight dots.

The *variable area-variable depth* process differs from the conventional gravure process just described in that the *size* of the cells as well as the *depth* varies to produce more durable tones in publication printing. The highlight cells (lighter areas) are shallower and smaller, while the shadow cells (darker areas) are deeper and larger. This process is used extensively for long runs in newspaper supplement and magazine printing.

A third method of gravure platemaking is the *direct transfer* or *variable area* method. A light-sensitive coating is first applied to the copper. The screened positive is wrapped around the cylinder and exposed directly to it by a strong light source usually through a narrow slit as the cylinder turns. The cylinder is then developed, and the coating which has not been struck by light is removed. We now have stencil or ink resistance in the non-printing areas as in other systems. The image elements on these cylinders vary in area but not in depth, so the number of tones is limited. This method is widely used in packaging and textile printing.

A major problem in gravure cylinder production has been

THREE TYPES OF GRAVURE

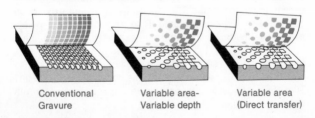

Conventional
Gravure

Variable area-
Variable depth

Variable area
(Direct transfer)

the unpredictability of tone values due to variations in the etching process. A number of attempts are being made to correct this. One approach is to use controlled etching such as in the Acigraf process and powderless etching as used in photo-engraving. Another is the method of electromechanical engraving, such as the Helioklischograph. Research is being done on the use of electron-beam and laser etching which are considerably faster.

Gravure cylinders are chromium plated for long runs. On very long runs the chromium can be worn off by friction of the doctor blade. In such cases the cylinder is removed, rechromed, and replaced in the press for continuing the run.

SCREEN PRINTING

There are many methods of making screens for screen printing. As previously mentioned, the screen consists of a porous material, and the printed image is produced by controlling the holes or *pores* of the screen.

Early screens were made by painting the image on silk mounted on a wooden frame. Masking materials were used to block out unwanted printing areas. Today, both hand-cut stencils and photomechanical means are used. One method is coating the material with a light-sensitive emulsion. Exposure is made through a film positive placed in contact with the screen. The screen surface is hardened in proportion to the degree of penetration of light, and the hardened areas are made insoluble to water. But the image remains water soluble which dissolves in development uncovering the screen through which the ink flows during printing.

Rotary screens The latest method is rotary screens which are made by plating the cylinder electrolytically on a steel cylinder, removing the cylinder after plating, applying a photomechanical coating to the cylinder, exposing it through a positive and a screen and etching out the image areas to form pores in the cylinder. On rotary screen presses the ink is pumped into the cylinder and the squeegee is also inside the cylinder.

PLATES FOR REPROGRAPHY

Electrophotographic plates For duplicating, or reprography as it is called, some printing systems use plates made by electrophotographic means. The Xerox method uses a selenium plate in which the selenium coating is charged with a corona discharge in a camera prior to the image being exposed. The image on the selenium is covered with a dry toner which is subsequently transferred to a metal or paper plate and fixed by heat or solvent. The metal or paper is then treated with special solutions for printing.

Another method uses the electrofax principle in which zinc oxide dispersed in a binder is coated on paper or metal. This is charged with a corona discharge and exposed in a camera to produce the printing image. Toner is applied to the exposed plate either in dry form or in an organic solvent like isopar. After development the toner in the image is fixed by heat or solvent vapor and the non-image area is treated with a ferrocyanide solution to make it water receptive. There are a number of copier/duplicators on the market that use this type of plate.

Direct image plates can be prepared by typing, drawing or lettering directly onto a paper master using special ribbons, pencils, and inks. Although inexpensive and easy to make, they are limited in quality and are used only for short runs.

Photographic plates There are two types of silver emulsion plates used for reprography. One is the 3M Camera Plate System in which the plate is made directly in the camera, processed and mounted on the press. It is capable of runs up to 1,000.

The other is based on the Kodak Verilith plate which consists of two photographic emulsions, and a third coating containing photographic developer coated on a paper base. During exposure development and fixing, a plate is produced in which the unexposed or image areas of the copy are tanned and become ink receptive, whereas the exposed or non-image areas remain water receptive. The plate has a rather critical ink-water balance, but it is used successfully on the Itek Platemaster, A-M Photo-Direct and A.B. Dick Photomat systems.

Diffusion transfer plates This is the principle of Polaroid film. A number of plates using this principle have been developed and used for reprography. The latest in this area is the Kodak PMT family of materials which can be used for conventional lithography as well as reprography. The letters PMT stand for Photomechanical Transfer. The family consists of a negative camera-speed paper; a reflex paper; receiver materials, and a metal litho plate. The receiver materials and plate have a special coating which receives the image from the exposed negative or reflex paper. A special processor and solutions are used. The new Kodak PMT metal litho plate is capable of runs up to 25,000 and could become an important factor in the successful use of conventional projectors in the new projection stripping method described on page 99.

printing

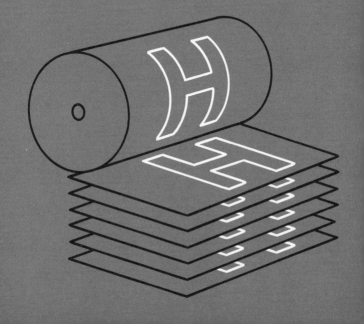

Printing presses are the production machines of the Graphic Arts industry. They are mass production machines designed to handle the needs of a mass production society. There are many different kinds, but it is nevertheless possible to isolate basic features that are found in all modern printing presses.

In general, a printing press must provide for: secure and precise mounting of the image carrier (and, in lithography, a blanket); accurate positioning of the paper during printing; conveying the paper through the printing units to the delivery; storing and applying ink (and, in lithography, a dampening solution) to the plate; accurately setting printing pressures for transfer of the inked image to the paper; and storing blank, partially-printed, and printed paper.

Presses are either sheet-fed or roll- (web-) fed. Much commercial work is printed on *sheet-fed presses*. Magazines, newspapers, books and some commercial work, are printed on web-fed presses. Presses may be single color or multicolor. Usually each color on a multicolor press requires a separate complete printing unit consisting of inking, plate and impression mechanisms. A two-color press would have two such units, a four-color press would have four, etc. Some presses share a common impression mechanism among two or more printing units and are known as *common impression cylinder* (CIC) presses, or satellite presses. Packaging and other special purpose equipment may have combinations of lithographic, letterpress and gravure units. A perfecting press is one which prints both sides of the paper in one pass through the press.

LETTERPRESS

There are three types of letterpress presses: *platen, flat-bed cylinder* and *rotary*.

Platen Press

The platen press carries both the type form and the paper on flat surfaces. These two surfaces, known as the *platen* and the *bed,* open and close somewhat like the jaws of a clamshell. The bed holds the type form; the platen holds the paper. As the jaws of the press open, the type form is inked and a sheet of paper is fed to the platen. As the jaws close, the sheet is printed. When they open again, the printed sheet is delivered and a new sheet is fed to the platen.

On most presses the amount of impression or *squeeze* is controlled by an impression lever. This ability to regulate the amount of squeeze makes the platen press extremely versatile. While this type of press is not suitable for printing books or high

THREE TYPES OF LETTERPRESS

| Platen | Flat-bed Cylinder | Rotary |

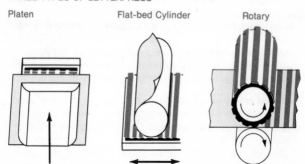

quality color work, it is ideal for job printing such as circulars, announcements, invitations, name cards, stationery, etc. Larger platen presses are used for embossing, die cutting and scoring.

Flat-bed Cylinder Press

In these presses, a moving flat bed holds the form while a fixed rotating impression cylinder provides the pressure. The paper, held securely to the cylinder by a set of steel clamps known as *grippers*, is rolled over the form as the bed passes under the cylinder. As the bed returns to its original position, the cylinder is raised, the form re-inked, and the printed sheet delivered.

On *vertical presses* (named because the bed is in a verti-cal position) both the form and the cylinder move up and down in a reciprocating motion. This cuts the usual two-revolution flat-bed motion in half; the impression cylinder makes only one revolution for every printed impression.

With the exception of the vertical press, the flat-bed cylinder press is becoming obsolete. It is not manufactured anymore in the U.S.

Rotary Press

This is the fastest and most efficient of the three types of let-terpress machines and is used mainly for long runs. Some large sheet-fed rotaries are still used for packaging. However, due to the declining market, the rotary press, like the flat-bed cylinder press, is no longer manufactured in the U.S.

On rotary presses both the impression and printing sur-faces are cylindrical: the plate cylinder holds the plates, and the impression cylinder provides the pressure. The sheet is printed with *each* revolution of the impression cylinder, as op-posed to the flat-bed method of printing with *every other* revolution.

Plates for rotary presses must be curved to the circumference of the plate cylinder, and electros and stereos are mostly used. Flexible plates can be used if mounted to rigid saddles or secured to a thin metal sheet fastened to the plate cylinder. There has been considerable development in recent years in lighter-weight curved plates and photopolymer plates which are known as direct printing plates.

Web-fed rotary press prints a continuous roll or *web* of paper on both sides as it passes through the press. One side is printed and dried first, as opposed to the blanket-to-blanket web offset press which prints both sides of the paper at the same time. These presses are used for all types of printing, from newspapers to fine color work in magazines and catalogs.

In newspaper presses, multiple printing couples (term used to describe a paired impression and plate cylinder) can be used, each couple perfecting a single web, and the multiple webs are assembled and folded in a single folder.

Most multicolor web-fed rotaries are of the common impression type. Special inks and dryers are used. The presses are operated at speeds of up to 1800 feet per minute. The paper is fed with automatic on-the-run splicing from one roll to another. The printed web is either sheeted or folded into signatures at the delivery end of the press.

The curved plates on these presses are held to the plate cylinder by means of movable clips or hooks. The latest presses use magnetic cylinders and steel-based plates.

Flexographic Press

Flexographic presses are also web-fed letterpress machines. There are three types: (1) *Stack type* in which two or three printing units are placed vertically in stacks. A press may consist of two or three stacks, with unwind, rewind, sheeter or cutter and creaser; (2) *Central impression cylinder* which is like the common impression system of rotary letterpress and is used extensively for printing flexible films; (3) *In-line* which is similar to a unit type rotary press.

Flexography uses rubber plates and water- or solvent-based inks in simple two-roller inking systems. It is an inexpensive and simple printing process used extensively for decorating and packaging printing. Quality has not been a prime objective, but recently good quality printing, including up to 150-line halftones, has been achieved on paper and flexible films by using special plates and reverse angle doctor blades on inking rollers in central impression cylinder presses.

There are limitations in the flexographic process which must be recognized. Hairline register, closed type faces and small type (under 6-pt.) should be avoided. Reverse type should be larger than 8-pt. and as bold as possible. Until distortion cameras were developed, special artwork was necessary to allow for the stretch and shrinkage of rubber in one direction which caused distortion of the image.

Makeready

One of the problems of letterpress printing is the variable pressure exerted by different size image elements in printing. The same amount of pressure, or *squeeze,* needed for ink transfer exerts greater pressure on small highlight dots than on larger shadow dots. Makeready evens out the impression so that highlights print correctly and do not puncture the paper. Precision electros, wraparound plates and premakeready systems help reduce makeready time.

In flexography, the rubber plate distorts and compresses, makeready is not too critical, and the process is easier to carry out. However, the distortion limits the quality of the screened image that can be printed and the register that can be maintained.

OFFSET LITHOGRAPHY

The offset press is responsible for the following important advantages in lithography: (1) the rubber printing surface conforms to irregular printing surfaces, resulting in the need for less pressure, improved print quality, and halftones of good quality on rough surfaced papers; (2) paper does not contact the metal plate, increasing plate life and reducing abrasive wear; (3) the image on the plate is straight reading rather than reverse reading; (4) less ink is required for equal coverage, drying is speeded up, and smudging and set-off are reduced.

The Offset Press

All offset presses operate on the principle of making one impression with *each* revolution of the cylinders. Sheet-fed offset presses have three same-size printing cylinders (plate, blanket and impression) as well as inking and dampening systems *(see illustration, page 33).* The plate is clamped to the plate cylinder. In rotating, it comes in contact with the *dampening* rollers first, then the *inking* rollers. The dampeners wet the plate so the non-printing area will repel ink. The inked image is then transferred to the rubber blanket on the blanket cylinder. Paper is printed as it passes between the blanket and impression cylinders.

OFFSET PRESS

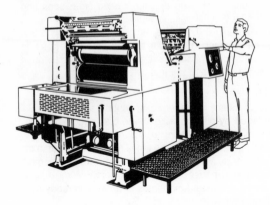

Makeready is minimal; the image is on a one-piece plate which can be shifted slightly for proper register. The resilient rubber blanket compensates for the varying thicknesses and textures of paper stocks, largely eliminating a source of considerable trouble in other printing processes. A wide range of papers can be used. Halftones can be printed with solids on both rough and smooth papers.

Sheet-fed presses are made in several sizes up to 55″ x 78″ which can print up to 7500 impressions per hour (iph). Some multicolor presses are manufactured in standard units that can be assembled in any number up to six units, for printing up to six colors. Most short-run color work is produced on one-color equipment; multicolor presses are generally used for long runs.

The conventional dampening system transfers the dampening solution directly to the plate. In the Dahlgren type of dampening system, the fountain solution containing up to 25% alcohol is metered to the plate through the inking system, or can be applied directly to the plate as in the Miehlematic system. In general, this type of dampening system uses less water and is said to reduce spoilage. A number of new fountain solutions have been developed to replace alcohol in this type of dampening system.

Sheet-fed perfecting presses are made in many sizes from 18½″ x 24½″ to 54″ x 77″. With two exceptions, these presses are all single color and utilize the *blanket-to-blanket* principle. One exception is a *convertible* press made in units from two to six colors. A two-unit convertible press prints either two colors on one side or one color on two sides, with minimum changeover time. A six-unit model has even more flexibility, printing six colors on one side; five colors on one side, one color on one side; four and two; etc.

Letterset (Dry Offset)

Like conventional offset, letterset uses a blanket for transferring the image from plate to paper. Unlike conventional offset, it uses a relief wraparound plate and requires no dampening system, thereby eliminating all water problems. Standard offset presses must be modified slightly for letterset because the plates are usually thicker. Because the inking is from a *raised* image, many refer to this process as *indirect letterpress*.

Other advantages of letterset are: quicker setting of inks, more consistent color throughout run, and somewhat higher ink gloss.

Web Offset

Much of the great expansion of the lithographic industry in recent years is attributed to the growth of web offset. Today, web offset produces single color and multicolor work for small and medium size newspapers, magazines, business forms, mail order catalogs, gift wrappings, books and encyclopedias, as well as commercial printing.

Speed is by far the main advantage of web offset. Speeds of 1000 feet per minute are common and special presses have been designed for speeds up to 1800 feet per minute and faster. Most web offset presses are 36" to 38" wide. Larger sizes up to 76" are specially built.

Much of the work produced on web offset presses proceeds to a folder where various combinations of folds convert the web into folded signatures. Other in-line operations that can be performed on press include paste binding, perforating, numbering, rotary sheeting and slitting. All of these make web offset very flexible, and all are done while presses are running at high speeds, from two to four times faster than sheet-fed offset.

The main disadvantage of web offset (and web letterpress, for that matter) is that it is limited to a fixed cut-off (i.e., all sheets cut off at the same length). A major advantage of rotogravure is that cylinders with different diameters can be readily interchanged on the press allowing for different cut-offs or image sizes. Some variable cut-off presses for web offset have been designed, but these are mainly for packaging or printing one side. Attempts to build variable cut-off blanket-to-blanket presses have proved to be very cumbersome, expensive and impractical.

Three Types of Web Offset Presses

(1) *The blanket-to-blanket press* has no impression cylinders. The blanket cylinder of one unit acts as the impression cylinder for the other, and vice versa. Each printing unit has two plate and two blanket cylinders. The paper is printed on *both* sides at the same time as it passes between the two blanket cylinders.

BLANKET-TO-BLANKET PRINTING UNIT

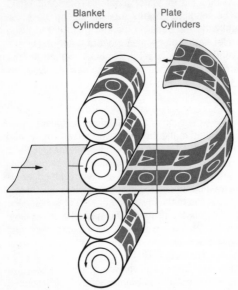

Blanket Cylinders   Plate Cylinders

(2) *The in-line open press* is similar to a sheet-fed offset press, except that the cylinder gap is very narrow. Grippers and transfer cylinders are eliminated. Each unit prints one color on one side; additional units are required for additional colors. To print the reverse side, the web is turned over between printing units by means of *turning bars,* which expose the unprinted side of the web to the remaining printing units. This type of press is used extensively for printing business forms.

(3) *The drum or common impression cylinder (CIC) press* has all the blanket cylinders grouped around a large common impression cylinder. This type of press is also called a satellite press. Two to five colors are printed in rapid succession on one side, after which the web is dried, turned, and the reverse side is printed in the same manner.

It is possible to print both sides on the same printing unit by a process known as *double ending.* A web one-half the width of the drum is printed, dried, turned over, and brought back through the other half of the drum for printing the reverse side.

Paper for web offset naturally has its grain direction paralleling the web. The printer and paper mill must work together on the specifications for each order. Rolls must be properly wound, protected, stored on end, and have good tensile strength to minimize tearing or breaking of the web on press. Paper should be of uniform caliper (thickness); be free from holes, slitter dust and lint; have a minimum of contraction and expansion; contain a minimum number of splices; and have sound cores for winding and delivery.

GRAVURE

A gravure printing unit consists of a printing cylinder, an impression cylinder, and an inking system. Ink is applied to the printing cylinder by an ink roll or spray, and the excess is removed by a doctor blade and returned to the ink fountain. The impression cylinder is covered with a resilient rubber composition that presses the paper into contact with the ink in the tiny cells of the printing surface.

Gravure inks are volatile and dry almost instantly. Driers are used between printing units to speed up drying. Therefore, in color printing each succeeding color is printed on a *dry color,* rather than on one which is still wet as in letterpress and offset.

For color printing, presses have automatic register control through the use of electric eyes which assure fidelity of color reproduction. Cylinders are chromium plated for press runs of a million or more. When the chromium begins to wear, it can be stripped off and the cylinder rechromed.

Gravure is currently used in packaging for quality color printing on transparent and flexible films and foils (any cut-off length is possible by changing the size of the printing cylinder); also, for printing cartons, including die-cutting and embossing which can be done in-line one run through the press.

All long-run mail order catalogs are printed by gravure. Among the interesting specialties printed by gravure are vinyl floor coverings, vinyl upholstery materials, pressure-sensitive wall coverings, plastic laminates, tax and postage stamps.

In the publication field, the largest rotogravure presses can print a web 106" wide; in the printing of floor coverings, multicolor gravure presses can print webs up to 150" wide. Presses used for packaging materials usually have webs from 40" to 60" wide with up to eight printing units. While speeds of 1500

GRAVURE PRESS

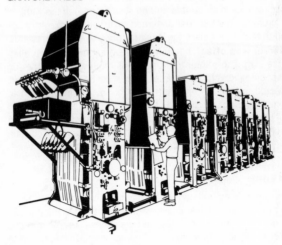

feet per minute and more are used in publication and catalog printing, average production speeds of up to 800 feet per minute are more realistic on other types of work.

Sheet-fed gravure presses operate on the same rotary principle as rotogravure. The preparatory work is identical. The image is etched flat on a flexible sheet of copper which is then clamped around the plate cylinder of the press. Sheet-fed gravure is primarily used for short runs. Because of the high quality and platemaking expense, it is used for art and photographic reproductions and prestige printing such as annual reports. In the packaging field, sheet-fed presses are used for printing new packages for market testing.

SCREEN PRINTING

Some screen printing is done today by hand with very simple equipment consisting of a table, screen frame and squeegee. However, most commercial screen printing is done on power-operated presses. There are both roll-fed and sheet-fed presses with hot air driers which run at speeds up to 300 feet per minute or over 4,000 impressions per hour.

There are two types of power-operated presses. One type uses flat screens which require an intermittent motion as each screen is printed. Butts and overlaps require close register, which limits running speed. The latest type uses rotary screens with the squeegee mounted inside the cylinder and the ink pumped in automatically. These presses are continuous running, fast and print continuous patterns with little difficulty.

The amount of ink applied is far greater than in letterpress, lithography, or gravure which accounts for some of the unusual effects in screen printing. Because of the heavy ink film, the sheets must be racked separately until dry, or passed through a heated tunnel or drier before they can be piled.

Screen printing prints on almost anything, and both line and halftone work can be printed. It is used for art prints, posters, decalcomania transfers, greeting cards, menus, program covers and wallpaper. Screen printing is important in the printing of textiles such as tablecloths, shower curtains and draperies. It is particularly adapted to the printing of leather, metal, glass, wood, ceramic materials and plastics, both flat and in finished molded form. By printing an adhesive size and then dusting with cotton, silk, or rayon flock, the finished design can be made to appear like felt or suede leather.

Screen printing has distinct advantages for short runs because of the simplicity of equipment needed. For longer runs, the advantage is soon lost since other printing methods are so much faster and more economical. However, for most of the applications listed, screen printing is the only practical process.

REPROGRAPHY

As described on pages 35-36, Reprography consists of all the processes used for making copies of original documents, books, etc. Copiers are the main equipment of reprography, but the offset duplicator is also an important piece of reprographic equipment which is described in greater detail here than in the previous reference.

Offset Duplicator

The offset duplicator is a small offset lithographic press which is used for fast, good quality reproduction of copies in sizes from 3″ x 5″ up to 14″ x 20″. Offset duplicators are ideal for low cost printing of business forms, letterheads, labels, bulletins, postcards, envelopes, folders, reports, catalogs, and sales literature. An average shop's output is probably about 50% informational, 40% forms, and 10% product.

Single-color jobs predominate, but a large amount of multicolor work is done and sometimes even four-color process jobs are printed. The original three-color process developed by Kodak used a duplicator for printing. Because of their versatility and speed, these presses are used in thousands of business, industrial, financial, educational, governmental and commercial printing plants. It is estimated that about 150,000 offset duplicators are used in in-plant printing shops alone, and another 30,000 to 40,000 in commercial plants.

Machines are made for simplified operation and convenience. The offset duplicator is a compact, heavy-duty, reliable, high production machine with many built-in features for fast job changeovers and minimum makeready. They can print on sheet stock from lightweight onionskin up to cardboard at speeds up to 9,000 impressions per hour (iph). Web duplicators are more limited in use, but are capable of speeds up to 25,000 iph.

OFFSET DUPLICATOR

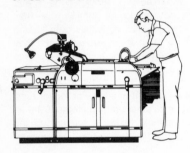

Besides the flexibility of quick changeover, duplicator presses can be equipped with attachments for etching *masters,* which are what duplicator plates are usually called, perforating, scoring, slitting, imprinting, numbering, embossing, printing a second color, perfecting, blanket washing, and master ejection. In-line attachments for collating, punching, and even dyeing the paper are some of the options offered for greater efficiency.

On the score of convenience, offset duplicators are better equipped than the larger offset press. For example, an ordinary photocopier can be put in line with the press, so that dry masters are delivered ready for inserting into the duplicator. Another feature is that up to 100 dry masters can be loaded into a tray on the duplicator and a program set. Then, at the press of a button, the machine prints the required number of prints and feeds master after master without further action on the part of the operator. The copies from each master are segregated from those above and below by automatic lateral angling of the machine's receiving tray. This means that the machine operator can proceed with imaging more masters while the press system works automatically.

binding

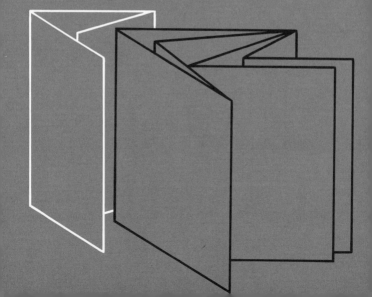

After paper is printed, some form of bindery or finishing operation usually follows, and this is the final processing of a printed piece. Most web printing, such as newspapers, will undergo some or all of their finishing steps on the press. Simple form work such as letterheads, business cards, etc., require no binding. However, most printing must be converted from large or small printed sheets to a finished printed piece, through various binding and finishing operations. The term finishing is used mostly for miscellaneous operations not necessarily part of the binding.

PAMPHLET BINDING

This is a rather general term for binding folders, booklets, catalogs, magazines, etc., as opposed to bookbinding which will be discussed later. There are generally five steps in pamphlet binding: *scoring, folding, gathering* or *collating, stitching,* and *trimming.* Most printing requires one or more of these, but not necessarily all. For example, a printed folder, the simplest form of pamphlet binding, is trimmed to size and folded. When printed sheets are delivered to the bindery, the first step is to fold the sheets (in multiples of 4s) into sections or *signatures.* In the case of heavy cover paper, folding is made easier by scoring.

Scoring

A score is defined as a crease in a sheet of heavyweight or cover paper to facilitate folding. As a rule, only those methods which produce an embossed ridge on the paper will give good folding results. The fold should always be made with the ridge or hinge on the inside for minimum stretch *(see illustrations).* Booklet or catalog covers must have a score wide enough to take the necessary number of pages without strain on the fold.

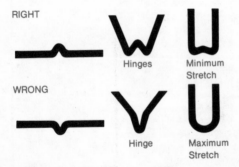

RIGHT

Hinges   Minimum Stretch

WRONG

Hinge   Maximum Stretch

The most common method of scoring is using a round face scoring rule locked in a form on a platen or cylinder press. The width of the rule varies with the thickness of the paper. A thicker paper requires a thicker rule which will give a wider crease to help make a cleaner fold.

Folding

Paper is usually folded on a *buckle type* folding machine. The sheet is carried along on conveyor belts from an automatic feeder, and steel rollers force the sheet into a fold-plate, which

FOLDER

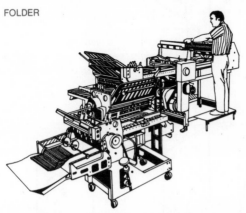

is adjustable to the length of the fold. The sheet hits a stop in the fold-plate, buckles, and is carried between two other rollers which fold the sheet. There can be as many as 64 pages to a signature.

There are two kinds of folds: *parallel* and *right angle*. Parallel folding is just what the name implies, each fold is parallel to the other. An example would be a letter which requires two parallel folds for mailing. An *accordion fold* is a type of parallel folding. A right angle fold is two or more folds, with each fold at right angles to the preceding one. For example, most formal invitations are folded with two right angle folds.

Folding machines can be equipped with attachments for scoring, trimming, slitting, perforating and pasting. These are generally inexpensive and time saving.

In designing printing, the different types of folds and the limitations of mechanical folding should be considered at the planning level. Otherwise, one or more folds might end up being a costly hand-folding operation. The sketches on the following page illustrate the most common types of folds.

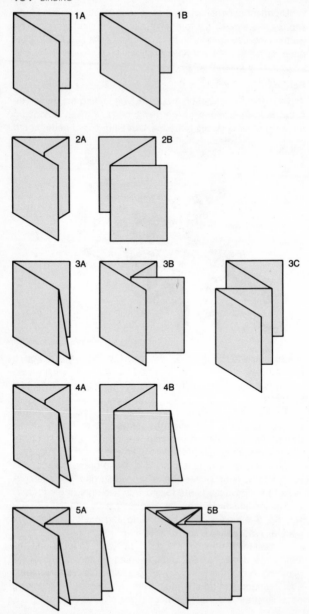

Types of Folders

1. Four-page folder Simplest type of folder, with only one fold, folding either on the (A) long or (B) short dimension. Used for bill stuffers, instruction sheets, price lists, etc.

2. Six-page folder Made with two parallel folds, either (A) regular or (B) accordion. Used for letters, circulars, envelope stuffers, etc.

3. Eight-page folder Illustrated in three ways, (A) one parallel and one right angle fold, also called *french fold* when printing is on one side of the paper, (B) two parallel folds and (C) three parallel accordion folds, for ease in opening. Also, (A) and (B) can be bound into an 8-page booklet.

4. Twelve-page folder Illustrated in two ways, both with one parallel fold and two right angle folds, either (A) regular or (B) accordion. Sometimes used as 4-page letter, with the two right angle folds folding letter to fit mailing envelope.

5. Sixteen-page folder Shown in two ways, (A) one parallel and two right angle folds and (B) three parallel folds, used for easy-to-open transportation schedules. Also, can be bound into a 16-page booklet.

Collating

Once folded, the next step is to gather or collate the signatures in a predetermined order. The collating order should be checked to be sure of the correct sequence. Collating can be done by hand or machine, depending on the size of the job.

Stitching

After the signatures are collated, they can be stitched together. There are two methods of stitching: *saddle-stitch* and *side-stitch*. The thickness or bulk of paper determines the style to be

SADDLE STITCHER

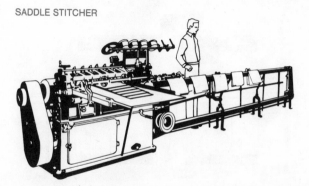

used. *Time* magazine is saddle-stitched; *House and Garden* is side-stitched.

In saddle-stitching, the booklet is placed on a saddle beneath a mechanical stitching head, and staples are forced through the backbone of the booklet. This type of binding is the simplest and most inexpensive. Booklets will lie flat and stay open for ease in reading. Most booklets, programs and catalogs are saddle-stitched.

SADDLE STITCH   SIDE STITCH

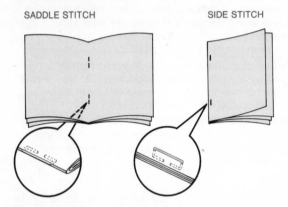

Side-stitching is used when the bulk is too great for saddle-stitching. The sections are collated, and then placed flat under a stitching head. Since the stitches are inserted about ¼" from the backbone, the inside margin must be wider than in a saddle-stitched booklet. Side-stitched books cannot be completely opened flat and often have glued-on covers.

PAPER CUTTER

Trimming or Cutting

Three sides (top, bottom, right) of the booklet are trimmed on a guillotine style paper cutter. For large-edition pamphlet binding, three-knife trimmers, which automatically trim three sides at one time are used. These are sometimes used as an attachment to the stitcher.

An automatic-spacing paper cutter is used for faster trimming of volume printing such as labels, leaflets, or any job printed in multiple form on the same sheet. This type of cutter automatically shifts to pre-set gauges after each cutting, resulting in greater uniformity and higher production.

BOOKBINDING

There are many ways to bind a book, but the most common methods are: *edition binding* (best when permanence is required), *perfect binding* (widely used for inexpensive paperback books) and *mechanical binding* (for manuals and notebooks).

Edition binding The conventional method, which has been in use for many years, starts with the folding of printed sheets into 16- or 32-page signatures. Four-page *endleaves* are pasted on the outside of the first and last signatures. The signatures are then collated by machine and sewn together by special sewing machines designed for this purpose.

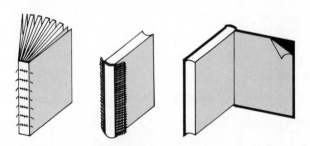

After they are sewn, the books are trimmed top, front and bottom, and the sewn edges are coated with glue. Each book is passed through a rounding machine which rolls the backbone. The rounded back is characteristic of this type of binding, and gives the book the correct shape to allow the cover to open and close properly. Next, a strip of gauze (super) is glued to the backbone in such a manner that the cloth extends outward from both sides of the backbone.

At the same time the books are being bound, the cloth covers *(cases)* are prepared on a case-making machine. Most covers are printed or stamped with some design and the title of the book. The printing is done on the cloth usually by the offset process and the stamping is done on a heavy-duty platen press using special dies and metallic foils. This is called *hot foil die stamping.* When the cover is finished, the book is automatically put into its case on a *casing-in* machine which applies paste to the endleaves and fits the cover into place.

The finished books are then dried in special hydraulic presses. Finally, they are inspected, wrapped in printed paper jackets, and packed for shipment. The school textbook and other hard bound books are examples of edition binding.

Perfect binding was developed to eliminate the expense of sewing and case-binding books. It is a variation of side-stitching and is widely used on paperback books. However, instead of being sewn or stitched, the pages are held together by a flexible adhesive. After the signatures are collated, the backs are ground off, leaving a rough surface. The adhesive is applied, a special lining is put over the backbone, and the cover is glued into place. The adhesive keeps its strength and resiliency for a long period of time. The *Pocket Pal* and the telephone book are examples of perfect binding.

PLASTIC   SPIRAL

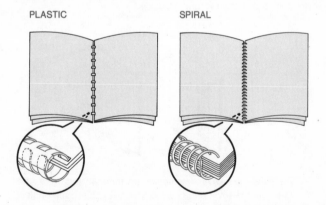

Mechanical binding is frequently used for notebooks and other types of books which must open flat. The sheets are punched with a series of round or slotted holes on the binding edge. Then wire, plastic coils or rings are inserted through the holes. Looseleaf notebooks are a form of mechanical binding with rings which open to allow the addition or replacing of pages. In designing a book for mechanical binding, allowance must be made in the gutter (inner margin) of the book for punching of the holes.

FINISHING

As previously mentioned, finishing is a general term that includes a number of different operations and specialties. For instance, mounting, die-cutting and easeling of displays; varnishing, laminating, embossing, bronzing, die-stamping, pebbling, punching, round cornering, padding, and tin-edging of printed and unprinted materials; cutting, creasing, stripping, and gluing of folding paper cartons; or slotting and gluing corrugated boxes. Most of these operations are highly specialized.

Some finishing operations are performed in-line with printing on web-fed presses. In newspaper, magazine and book printing, folded signatures are delivered from the press. In some types of packaging, particularly on flexographic presses, the cutting, creasing and stripping are done in-line with the printing. The new UV inks make possible in-line operations like lacquering, folding, slitting, etc., in sheet-fed printing.

Two finishing operations quite often used are embossing and die-cutting.

Embossing The image is molded in embossing so that it is raised in relief. Molding is achieved by pressing the material to be embossed between a brass female die and a male bed or counter mounted in register on a press. Strawboard, plastic, molding compound or newspaper matte material may be used for a counter. The counter is built up with layers of glued paper and shaped with an impression from the die on the press. All shoulders and squeezed material are cut away; pressure is applied only to the die area.

Light embossing may be done without heat on a cylinder or platen press. For heavy embossing and where fine detail is required, the die is fastened to a heated plate on a heavy duty arch or *four-post* press. Embossing may be done in register with printing, or on blank stock giving a bas-relief effect. The latter is called blind embossing, and a soft paper is best. If a metallic effect is desired, special stamping foil is used.

Die-cutting There are two methods in use today: high or hollow die-cutting and steel rule die-cutting. Hollow die-cutting is a process used almost exclusively for labels and envelopes. A steel die, which is hollow like a cookie cutter, is positioned on a jogged pile of printed sheets. Pressure forces the die through the pile. The labels remain in the die until stripped out by hand.

Steel rule die-cutting is used for larger size dies or where close register is required. The dies are hardened steel rules bent to a desired shape in ¾" plywood. The multiple dies are locked up in a chase. They are positioned and made ready on a platen die-cutting press much the same as in letterpress. The patching is done under a steel die-cutting jacket. Several sheets may be cut at one time using the start-and-stop method.

Flatbed cylinder presses are often used for die-cutting. The ink rollers are removed to avoid being cut, and a steel jacket is secured around the cylinder. Die-cutting jackets are available to fit most presses and can be readily attached. Dies must have small nicks to prevent the die-cut area from dropping out while on press.

Rotary die-cutters are also in use. They are more expensive and are used in specialty packaging such as milk cartons.

Shrink-packaging In recent years, shrink-packaging has been used more and more to replace kraft paper packaging and banding. In addition to being able to see the product through the wrapping, its advantages are increased production and reduced labor cost. The equipment is simple to operate and inexpensive. Three essential units are needed: (1) a work table for dispensing the film and inserting the product; (2) an "L" bar heat sealer; (3) a shrink tunnel. The product is inserted into a folded roll of polyethylene film which is heat-sealed around the product. It then goes into the shrink tunnel where the proper temperature shrinks the film tightly around the product. With proper equipment and film, almost any kind and shape of product can be shrink-packaged.

paper

Paper, paperboard, or other stock on which an image is printed usually represents 30%-50% of the final cost of a printed job. Besides the cost, the paper's characteristics can have a big bearing on the appearance of the job and the printer's ability to print it. Since paper is one of the most important parts of a printed piece, everyone involved should know as much as possible about its manufacture and characteristics so that the proper paper is selected. The paper selected should have the desired printability and runnability so that minimum problems are encountered in the printing.

PULPING

The first step in papermaking is the production of pulp, and wood is by far the most widely used raw material. In some parts of the world where wood is not readily available other fiber sources are utilized, such as bagasse (sugar cane), bamboo, esparto and hemp. There are essentially three types of pulping processes: *mechanical, chemical* and *semi-chemical*.

Mechanical pulping produces groundwood pulp. Cleaned and peeled logs are ground against a revolving grindstone or disc mill until they are reduced to fiber. Groundwood pulp is very economical since all the wood is used. It does however contain impurities which can cause discoloration and weakening of the paper. Its main use is for newsprint. It is also used as part of the pulp in magazine papers where it contributes bulk, opacity and compressibility.

Chemical pulping removes most of the lignin, resins, gums and other undesirable components of the wood so that the pulp is mainly cellulose fiber. Papers made from this pulp are much more permanent than groundwood paper. Chemical pulping is done by cooking wood chips with chemicals in batch or continuous digesters. There are two main types of chemical wood pulp: *sulfite* and *sulfate*. Sulfite pulp is made by cooking chips of coniferous woods like spruce, pine and hemlock in a liquor made from lime and sulfurous acid. Sulfate pulp, also known as kraft, is produced by cooking broadleaf or coniferous woods with caustic soda and sodium sulfide. Since sulfate or kraft pulp uses a wider variety of woods and produces a stronger paper, it is used more widely than sulfite pulp.

Semi-Chemical pulping combines chemical with mechanical pulping to produce a pulp with higher yield yet somewhat similar properties to chemical pulp. It is a treatment for hardwoods and is usually used as a blend with chemical pulp imparting stiffness and good formation.

BLEACHING

Bleaching is a further step in the purification of fibers and is responsible for higher brightness in papers. While pure cellulose is white in color, the presence of impurities and coloring matter gives the pulp a brownish color, as in grocery bags, which are made from unbleached kraft pulp. Chemical pulps are bleached in multiple stage processes (3-7 stages) with chemicals like chlorine, chlorine dioxide, and/or sodium hypochlorite, with alternate treatments in caustic soda and washing with water.

BEATING, REFINING AND SIZING

Beating and refining are important steps in papermaking since the characteristics of the paper are largely determined by the treatment of the pulp in these operations.

Beating is performed in an oval tub in which a large batch of pulp is circulated by means of a revolving roll. Refining is done in closed conical shaped units. In both cases the pulp is passed between a rotating and a stationary set of steel bars which cause cutting, bruising and crushing of the fibers. The treatment is controlled to produce the desired strength and other qualities in the finished paper. Refining is a continuous process permitting fast changes in paper characteristics and has largely replaced beating.

In addition to the mechanical treatment of the pulp, certain materials are added to impart other characteristics which make the product more suitable for its intended use. Rosin size is added to give water repellency so that the paper can be used for pen and ink writing, offset printing or resistance to weather. Fillers, such as clay, are used to improve smoothness, opacity and affinity for ink; titanium dioxide for opacity and brightness. Dyes and pigments are also added to control the color shade or to produce colored papers, and alum is added to fix the size and color on the fibers. The combination of fiber, size, fillers and alum is known as *stock,* and this is stored in large tanks or chests ahead of the paper machine.

MAKING PAPER

The modern Fourdrinier paper machine is extremely complex but consists essentially of three principal units: (1) the paper-forming section, known as the wet end (2) the press section, where water is removed by pressing the wet paper between rolls and felts and (3) the drying section, where the moisture content is reduced to the desired level.

Fourdrinier Wet End

The stock from the machine chest is diluted with water and pumped to a distribution unit or headbox. This spreads the flow to the width of the machine and discharges it thru an orifice onto a finely woven endless wire belt. The water is drained thru the wire by gravity and suction, leaving the stock on the surface. The fibers tend to align themselves in the direction the machine is traveling. To prevent this and improve the formation, the headbox end of the wire section is given a side-to-side shaking motion. Some machines, especially for offset newsprint, are equipped with two wires.

Dandy Roll

This roll consists of a cylindrical frame covered with wire mesh and is located on top of the wire between two of the suction boxes. At this point the sheet is still wet enough to be compressed by the weight of the roll which helps distribute the fibers and improve formation. In some cases the surface of the roll contains lettering or a design, and this type of dandy roll produces a watermarked paper.

Press Section

The web of paper as it leaves the wire still contains 75-85% of water, and this is reduced to 60-70% in the press section. The operation is performed in a series of presses, each consisting of two rolls, and the sheet passes thru the nip between these rolls supported on a felt made mainly of wool. Removal of water by

DRY END OF A PAPER MACHINE

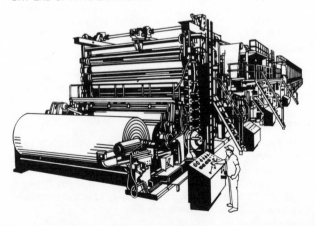

pressing is much more economical than by drying, and the presses compact the sheet and level the surface.

Machine Drying

From the presses the paper enters the drying sections where the sheet is dried to the final moisture content. The driers are steam-heated cast iron drums, four to six feet in diameter, polished on the outside surface. The drums are generally arranged in two tiers with as many as thirty tiers of driers on some of the larger installations. On paper machines the sheet is held tightly against the driers by a heavy felt usually made of cotton or cotton-asbestos combinations. About two pounds of water are evaporated for each pound of paper produced.

Calendering and Supercalendering

Calendering is the last operation on the paper machine before the paper is rolled on the reels. Supercalendering is a subsequent operation. Machine calenders are stacks of vertical cast steel rolls that have polished ground surfaces. The paper enters the stack at the top and is compacted and smoothed progressively as it travels on the way down the stack. Calendered papers are known as *machine finished papers*. Supercalenders are also arranged vertically, but the rolls are alternately steel and either cotton or compressed paper. Supercalenders are used for both coated and uncoated papers.

Coated Papers

The great popularity of reproducing black-and-white and color photographs brought about the development of coated papers. These grades reproduce much finer halftone screens with sharper definition, improved density and greater color fidelity than can be reproduced on uncoated papers. Coated paper finishes range from dull to very glossy, have a greater affinity for printing inks, greater smoothness, higher opacity, and better ink holdout than uncoated papers.

Coated printing papers are available coated one side only (C1S) for labels, packaging and covers; or coated two sides (C2S) for book, publication and commercial printing. Papers coated on the machine are called *machine coated;* those coated on independent coaters are said to be *off-machine coated.*

Coatings consist of suspensions of pigments in suitable binders. They are applied by rolls, air knives, or by trailing blades. Blade coatings have become very popular as they are smoother, and it is possible to apply lower coat weights which are necessary for lighter weight publication grades.

Paper Finishes

Finish is a complex paper property related to its smoothness. Paper can be used as it comes off the dryers of a paper machine, or it can be machine calendered and then later supercalendered. Uncalendered, machine calendered and supercalendered papers vary greatly in smoothness.

The usual finishes of uncoated book papers are, in order of increasing smoothness: *antique, eggshell, vellum, machine finish* (MF), and *English finish* (EF). These finishes are classed together because all can be produced on the machine. Additional smoothness is obtained with supercalendering. A frequently used grade is known as *super* or SC. Coating, of course, improves the finish and smoothness.

Some finishes are embossed on the paper after it leaves the machine. These are produced by a rotary embosser, a machine similar to a mangle, with the paper passing through it dry and under pressure. Commonly used embossing patterns are linen, tweed, and pebble.

Top (Felt) Side and Wire Side

Paper is considered a two-sided material. Each of its two sides has different characteristics. These are due to the way paper is made. The side directly in contact with the wire of the paper machine is called the *wire side,* the other side is the top or *felt side*. The felt side usually has a closer formation with less grain and better crossing of the fibers. The wire side however has less fines on the surface and usually gives less trouble with collecting loose paper dust or lint on the blanket of an offset press.

Some new paper machines have two wires and are known as twin-wire machines. The paper produced on these machines has less *two-sidedness* than paper produced on conventional machines. Both sides are more similar to the wire side in that they have less fines and cause less problems with lint on blankets on offset presses. They are used especially for newsprint in web offset printing.

PAPER CHARACTERISTICS

Grain is an important factor for both printing and binding. It refers to the position of the fibers. During papermaking most fibers are oriented with their length parallel to that of the paper machine and their width running across the machine. In other words, the grain of the sheet is in the *machine direction;* the other dimension is called the *cross direction.*

Grain affects paper in the following ways, and these facts need to be considered in the proper use of paper: (1) Paper

TEAR AND FOLD TESTS

Paper tears straighter with grain

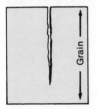 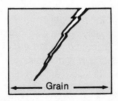

Paper folds more easily with grain

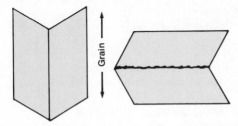

folds smoothly *with* the grain direction and roughens or cracks when folding cross-grain. This is often important in planning a printed piece. (2) Paper is stiffer in the grain direction. (3) Paper expands or contracts more in the cross direction when exposed to moisture changes.

In books and catalogs, grain direction should be parallel with the binding edge. If it is perpendicular with the binding edge, the pages turn less easily and do not lie flat. Paper for sheet-fed offset is usually grain long. Moisture changes affect the shorter dimension and register problems are reduced. A second reason for grain long is that the sidewise size of printed images cannot be changed without cutting or changing plates, whereas changing the size of the printed image around the cylinder (short dimension of the sheet) can be accomplished by changing the packing under the plate and blanket.

Basis weight With few exceptions, printing papers are manufactured and identified by their *basis weight*. By definition, it is the weight in pounds of a ream (500 sheets) in the *basic size* for that grade. For example (knowing the basic size of book paper is 25 x 38), basis 70 means that 500 sheets 25 x 38 of book paper weighs 70 pounds.

The basic size is *not* the same for all grades: 25 x 38 for book paper (coated, text, offset, opaque, etc.); 17 x 22 for writing papers (bond, ledger, mimeograph, duplicator); 20 x 26 for cover papers (coated and uncoated); 25½ x 30½ for index bristol, 22½ x 28½ or 22½ x 35 for mill bristol and postcard; 24 x 36 for tag and newsprint.

Paper is commonly referred to in terms of its ream weight: 20-pound bond, 70-pound coated, etc. However, paper is usually listed in sizes-and-weight tables and price lists on a thousand sheet basis: 25 x 38–140M for a 70-pound book paper, the "M" meaning 1,000 sheets 25 x 38 weigh 140 pounds.

Each grade is made in many standard sizes other than the basic size, and in many weights. For example, book papers are made in weights from 50-pound to 100-pound in 10-pound increments.

In the Metric System (used today by most other countries) basis weight or substance is referred to as *grammage*. Basis weight is expressed as weight per unit area, or grams per square meter (gsm or g/m^2). Such a measurement is independent of paper size and is now accepted as a preferred system by the Technical Assn. of the Pulp & Paper Industry (TAPPI).

Thickness and bulk Thickness is often referred to as caliper and is measured in mils or thousandths of an inch. In book manufacturing, the bulk of the paper determines the thickness of the book so it is often expressed in different terms than the thickness or caliper of the sheet. Bulk for book papers is expressed as the number of pages per inch for a given basis weight. For example, the bulking range for a 50 pound (500 sheets of 25 x 38) book paper can be from 310 to 800 pages per inch.

Strength The strength of paper is more dependent on the nature of its fiber than its thickness. High bursting strength is achieved by closely intermingling long pulp fibers during the forming of the sheet on the paper machine wire. Some papers, paper bags for example, need high tearing resistance. Fibers are long, and tear in the cross-machine direction is always higher than tear in the machine direction. This is so because the greatest number of fibers lie *across* the path of the cross-machine tear.

Papers which are subjected to considerable tension in use, such as those printed on web presses, should have a high tensile strength as well as high tear strength.

Stretch is the amount of distortion paper undergoes under tensile strain. Stretch is generally much greater in the cross direction than in the machine direction.

RUNNABILITY AND PRINT QUALITY

Two important factors that affect the printing of papers by any process are *runnability* and *print quality*. Runnability affects the ability to get the paper through the press and failures in runnability can cause expensive downtime. Print quality factors affect the appearance of the print on the paper.

Runnability

This is more of a problem in offset than in letterpress or gravure because of the overall contact of the paper with the blanket during impression, and the use of water and tacky inks. The following paper properties can affect runnability:

Flatness Freedom from buckles, puckers, wave and curl – especially important in offset.

Trimming Sheets should be square, accurate in size.

Dirt Loose material from all manufacturing sources, such as slitter and trimmer dust, loose pigments or loosely bonded fibers on the surface – especially troublesome in offset.

IMPROPERLY CONDITIONED PAPER

Wavy edges   Tight edges

Moisture content or RH The paper should be in balance with the pressroom RH. An increase in RH can cause *wavy edges;* the edges absorb moisture while the rest of the pile remains unchanged. *Tight edges,* in which the edges lose moisture and contract, are caused when the RH of the pressroom is lower than the paper. Both wavy and tight edges can cause wrinkles and/or misregister in printing, especially in offset.

Adequate pick resistance Weak paper surfaces tend to pick, blister, or split when tacky ink is transferred from the plate or blanket to the paper. This is more of a problem in offset than letterpress.

Adequate water resistance Lithographic papers with soluble or water-sensitive coatings tend to pile on the blanket necessitating frequent stops for washups. The piling can occur in the image or non-image areas. Each is caused by different paper properties, and the exact cause is not known for sure.

Paper-ink relationships Paper surfaces can affect ink drying, chalking, set-off, ink and varnish holdout.

Mechanical condition Paper should be free of holes, wrinkles, torn sheets, scraps, turned-over corners, stuck spots or edges and foreign matter. Paper rolls should be evenly and tightly wound with smooth even edges and a minimum of splices.

Print Quality

The appearance characteristics of the print can be affected by the following paper properties. These are especially important when the same job is being printed in more than one plant or when a job is being reprinted.

Color Paper color is important as it affects the color reproduction of lighter tints especially. Paper colors vary with advertising fads from cool to warm shades. Type is most easily read against a soft (yellowish) white, while process colors reproduce most accurately on neutral white paper.

Brightness affects the contrast, brilliance, snap or sparkle of the printed subject. Artificial brighteners, like fluorescent additives, can affect color reproduction as most are not neutral in color and have excess blue reflectance.

Opacity relates to the "show-through" of the printed image from the opposite side of the sheet or the adjoining sheet. It is affected by the thickness of the sheet and the use of mineral fillers like titanium dioxide.

Smoothness is a very important property for letterpress and gravure but has little effect on offset. Smooth surfaces have irregularities of the order of 0.005" to 0.010" apart. They cannot be seen by the naked eye, but can be detected by a magnifying glass and low angle illumination. As smoothness decreases, solids and halftones get sandy and rough in appearance but type is not affected much.

Gloss affects the appearance of the ink film. Coupled with ink absorption, it can be used as a measure of paper surface efficiency (PSE) or the purity of ink reproduction.

Refractiveness relates to light absorption in the surface of the paper causing halftones to appear darker than they should.

PAPER TESTING AND EVALUATION FOR PRINTABILITY

Printing papers are tested for a number of properties, namely, basis weight, brightness, caliper, gloss, oil absorption, opacity, porosity, smoothness, stiffness, tear, tensile strength. While all of these tests are valuable for mill quality control and product uniformity, they are generally useless for predicting the printing characteristics of the paper. Much printability testing has been done, and many testers have been designed and built. But the most reliable testing for lithography, especially, is still done on a production press.

Most letterpress testing for smoothness, ink receptivity, and coverage can be done on a proof press like the Vandercook Universal Test Press. The IGT Printability Tester can be used to make reasonably accurate predictions of picking, ink coverage, receptivity, and, with the new Universal model, even trapping has been predicted with some degree of success. There are several printability testers for gravure.

For lithography, however, printability testers are far from having the reliability desired. Most printability testing is done on an offset press. Many laboratories are working on the development of bench or proof press tests that correlate with performance on the press. As yet none has been completely successful.

PAPER GRADES

Paper may be defined in terms of its use. Each grade serves a purpose, usually suggested by its grade name. Some of the most common classifications of printing papers are: bond, coated, text, cover, book, offset, index, label, tag and newsprint. The size shown in parentheses is the basic size for that particular grade.

Bond (17 x 22) Papers commonly used for letters and business forms. They have surfaces which accept ink readily from a pen or typewriter and which can be easily erased. Most letterheads and business forms are a standard 8½ x 11 size. Four pieces this size can be cut from a 17 x 22 sheet without waste.

Coated (25 x 38) This is base paper which has been given a smooth, glossy coating. Coated papers are used when high printing quality is desired because of its greater surface smoothness and uniform ink receptivity. There are many kinds: cast coated, dull coated, machine coated, coated one side, etc.

Text (25 x 38) These papers are noted for their interesting textures and attractive colors. They enjoy frequent use for announcements, booklets and brochures. Most text papers are treated with a sizing to make them more resistant to water penetration and easier to print by offset lithography.

Book (25 x 38) As the name implies, these papers are used for trade and textbooks. They are less expensive than text papers, and are made in antique or smooth finishes. Book papers have a wider range of weights than text papers so it is possible to secure almost any desired bulking.

Offset (25 x 38) Similar to the coated and uncoated book paper used for letterpress printing except that sizing is added to resist the slight moisture present in offset printing, and the surface is treated to resist picking. While most offset papers may be printed letterpress, few letterpress papers are suitable for offset.

Cover (20 x 26) Quite often coated and text papers are made in heavier weights and matching colors which are used as covers on booklets, etc. There are also papers made for cover purposes only. Many surface textures are available, with finishes ranging from antique to smooth including many special finishes. Special characteristics of cover papers include dimensional stability, uniform printing surface, good folding qualities and durability.

Index (22½ x 35 and 25½ x 30½) Two outstanding characteristics are stiffness and receptivity to writing ink. Commonly used whenever an inexpensive stiff paper is required. Available in both smooth and antique finish.

Newsprint (24 x 36) Paper used in printing newspapers. Furnish is chiefly groundwood pulp, with some chemical pulp. It is made in basis weights from 28 to 35 pounds; with 30-pound used most extensively.

Tag (24 x 36) A cylinder or fourdrinier sheet ranging in weight from 100 to 250 pounds suitable for the manufacture of tags. It may be made from sulfite, sulfate or mechanical pulp, and various types of waste papers. Tag board is sometimes tinted and colored on one or both sides. Tag stock has good bending or folding qualities, suitable bursting and tensile strength, good tearing and water resistance, and a surface adaptable to printing, stamping, or writing.

Tips when Ordering Paper

Anticipate your needs well in advance. This applies to standard sizes and weights, as well as special-making orders in sheets or rolls. Your merchant represents several paper mills, and cannot be expected to carry the many thousands of stock items. In ordering paper try to combine items from the same mill. Special sizes and weights have to be made to order and take longer for delivery. When paper is changed on a job, especially a rerun, it is advisable to check color and printability as these could affect the appearance of the final result.

CUTTING CHARTS

A good paper buyer always tries to use standard paper sizes which can be used without waste. Odd size pages can be wasteful and costly if the quantity is not large enough, or if there is not enough time, to order a special-making size of paper. Bear this in mind in planning a proposed printing piece.

The chart on this page shows the number of pages to a standard paper size for several page sizes in use today. The paper size includes trim top, bottom and side. However, it does *not* include bleed.

Trimmed Page Size	Number of Printed Pages	Number From Sheet	Standard Paper Size
	4	12	25 x 38
	8	12	38 x 50
4 x 9	12	4	25 x 38
	16	6	38 x 50
	24	2	25 x 38
	4	32	35 x 45
4¼ x 5³⁄₈	8	16	35 x 45
	16	8	35 x 45
	32	4	35 x 45
	4	16	25 x 38
4½ x 6	8	8	25 x 35
	16	4	25 x 38
	32	2	25 x 38
	4	16	35 x 45
5½ x 8½	8	8	35 x 45
	16	4	35 x 45
	32	2	35 x 45
	4	8	25 x 38
6 x 9	8	4	25 x 38
	16	2	25 x 38
	32	2	38 x 50
	4	4	23 x 35
8½ x 11	8	2	23 x 35
	16	2	35 x 45
	4	4	25 x 38
9 x 12	8	2	25 x 38
	16	2	38 x 50

EQUIVALENT WEIGHTS

In reams of 500 sheets, basis weights in bold type

Grade of Paper	BOOK 25 x 38	BOND 17 x 22	COVER 20 x 26	BRISTOL 22½ x 28½	INDEX 25½ x 30½	TAG 24 x 36	GRAMMAGE (gsm)
BOOK	**30**	12	16	20	25	27	44
	40	16	22	27	33	36	59
	45	18	25	30	37	41	67
	50	20	27	34	41	45	74
	60	24	33	40	49	55	89
	70	28	38	47	57	64	104
	80	31	44	54	65	73	118
	90	35	49	60	74	82	133
	100	39	55	67	82	91	148
	120	47	66	80	98	109	178
BOND	33	**13**	18	22	27	30	49
	41	**16**	22	27	33	37	61
	51	**20**	28	34	42	46	75
	61	**24**	33	41	50	56	90
	71	**28**	39	48	58	64	105
	81	**32**	45	55	67	74	120
	91	**36**	50	62	75	83	135
	102	**40**	56	69	83	93	151
COVER	91	36	**50**	62	75	82	135
	110	43	**60**	74	90	100	163
	119	47	**65**	80	97	108	176
	146	58	**80**	99	120	134	216
	164	65	**90**	111	135	149	243
	183	72	**100**	124	150	166	271
BRISTOL	100	39	54	**67**	81	91	148
	120	47	65	**80**	98	109	178
	148	58	81	**100**	121	135	219
	176	70	97	**120**	146	162	261
	207	82	114	**140**	170	189	306
	237	93	130	**160**	194	216	351
INDEX	110	43	60	74	**90**	100	163
	135	53	74	91	**110**	122	203
	170	67	93	115	**140**	156	252
	208	82	114	140	**170**	189	328
TAG	110	43	60	74	90	**100**	163
	137	54	75	93	113	**125**	203
	165	65	90	111	135	**150**	244
	192	76	105	130	158	**175**	284
	220	87	120	148	180	**200**	326
	275	109	151	186	225	**250**	407

Comparative Weights of Book Papers per 1,000 Sheets

Basis	50	60	70	80	100	120
8½ x 11	9.8	11.8	13.8	15.7	19.7	23.6
17½ x 22½	41	50	58	66	83	99
19 x 25	50	60	70	80	100	120
23 x 29	70	84	98	112	140	169
23 x 35	85	102	119	136	169	203
24 x 36	90	110	128	146	182	218
25 x 38	100	120	140	160	200	240
35 x 45	166	198	232	266	332	398
36 x 48	182	218	254	292	364	436
38 x 50	200	240	280	320	400	480
*metric (gsm)	74	89	104	118	148	178

ENVELOPE STYLES

A. Commercial envelopes are used for business correspondence, either surface or airmail. Made in bond and kraft papers in all standard sizes.

B. Window envelopes are used primarily for statements and invoices. The window saves time and prevents an element of error by eliminating typing of an extra address. Window envelopes are made in all sizes, papers and styles.

C. Self-Sealing envelopes have latex adhesive on upper and lower flaps that seal instantly without moisture when flaps come together. These envelopes are a time saver in handling.

D. Booklet, Open-Side envelopes are ideal for direct mail and house organs. Concealed seam lends itself to overall printing in front and back.

E. Baronial envelopes are a more formal open-side envelope with a deep, pointed flap. They are often used for invitations, greeting cards, announcements, etc.

F. Bankers Flap and Wallet Flap envelopes handle unusually bulky correspondence. Can be crammed with correspondence and will carry material safely. Reserve strength is far in excess of everyday commercial envelopes.

G. Clasp and String-and-Button envelopes are sturdy and widely used for mailing bulky papers. Metal clasps are smooth and burrless. String and button keep contents under tension and better protected in the mail. Both types may be opened and closed many times.

*Metric equivalent of basis weight.

H. Open End envelopes are used for mailing catalogs, reports, booklets and magazines. Wide seams and heavy gummed flaps insure maximum protection under rough handling conditions.

I. Expansion envelopes are used for bulky correspondence and for package and rack sales.

ENVELOPE STYLES

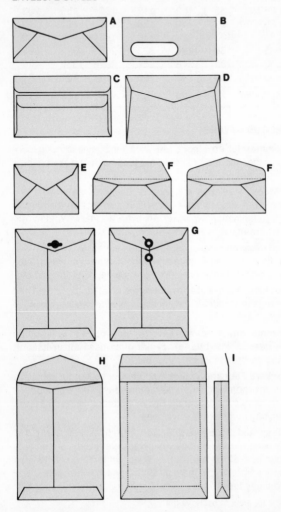

printing inks

The ingredients used to manufacture printing inks fall into three main classifications: fluid ingredients or *vehicles* and *solvents*, solid ingredients or *pigments*, and miscellaneous other ingredients (principally driers and compounds). Pigments are fine particles which impart the color to an ink—whether black, white, or any of the common colors.

The most important properties of ink besides color and color strength are *body, length, tack* and *drying* characteristics.

Body refers to the consistency, stiffness or softness of inks. Ink consistencies vary widely from very stiff inks for collotype to very soft, fluid inks for newsprint, gravure and flexography. Associated with the body is the term *viscosity* which is a means of controlling soft or fluid inks. Stiff inks can have a false body which is called *thixotropy*. Conventional letterpress and offset inks are thixotropic. They set to a fairly stiff mass in the can but when they are worked on a slab with an ink knife they become quite fluid and flow freely.

Length is a property associated with the ability of an ink to flow and form filaments. Inks can be *long* or *short*. Long inks flow well but form long filaments. They are undesirable, especially on high speed presses because they have a tendency to *fly*. Newsprint inks are characterized by this property. Short inks have the consistency of butter with poor flow properties. They have a tendency to pile on the rollers, plate or blanket.

LONG INK   SHORT INK

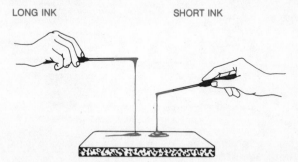

Tack is the *stickiness* of the ink, or the force required to split an ink film between two surfaces. It is an important requirement in the transfer of ink from the inking rollers to the plate and then from the plate to the paper in letterpress or from the plate to the blanket and the blanket to the paper in offset. Tack is also important in determining whether the ink will pick the surface of the paper, will trap properly in wet multicolor printing, or will

INKOMETER

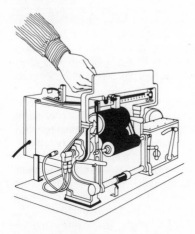

print sharp clean lines and halftones. If the tack of the ink is higher than the surface strength of the paper, the paper will pick, split or tear. In wet multicolor printing the first ink down must be tackier than the next ink at the instant of transfer, or the second ink will not transfer to (trap on) the first color. Offset inks must be tacky to print sharp images and resist emulsification with the fountain solution. Compromises must be reached when jobs contain both solids and halftones since tacky inks do not print good solids. Ink tack can be measured with an Inkometer or Tackoscope.

Drying of inks is important because a printed piece cannot be handled or used until the liquid or plastic ink film has solidified and dried. Printing inks dry in a number of ways: absorption, selective absorption, oxidation, polymerization, evaporation and precipitation. Most inks dry by a combination of two or more of these mechanisms.

New systems for drying or curing inks have been developed to eliminate pollution caused by the evolution of solvents and other pollutants associated with ink drying. New solventless inks that cure by crosslinking and UV radiation are described in the section on Solventless Inks *(page 162)*. New infrared units have been developed for drying inks on sheet-fed presses using inks of the low solvent type. Also water and alcohol soluble coatings are being used to overcoat wet inks immediately after printing. The coatings dry rapidly, keeping the inks from scuffing or marking while they dry normally.

Planning When a job is first planned, "thinking ink" can avoid a lot of later headaches and expense. Remember that the ink-maker must mate the ink to the paper. Their relationship is critical. Color matches for small amounts of ink for short runs can be expensive. Also left-over ink is frequently of no use. Leading inkmakers now offer a kit of 6 to 8 basic inks with color chart and instructions, and with these inks upwards of 400 colors can be mixed from the formulas provided.

Samples of paper to be used are a must when ordering inks. If this cannot be done, the next best thing is to tell the inkmaker what grade the paper will be. However, when printing on a specially treated paper or one that has an unusual printing surface, the printer must send samples to the inkmaker. In addition, the inkmaker should know the printing process, color rotation, type of press, press speed, drying demands, gloss, varnish, and any special requirements such as alcohol or alkali proof, fade resistant, etc. *(see Special Characteristics, page 164).*

Letterpress Inks

Letterpress inks are designed for printing from raised surfaces such as type, engravings and electrotypes. These inks are usually of moderate tack and viscosity.

Printers are most familiar with letterpress inks that dry by oxidation. These are in paste form and consist mainly of pigments and drier ground in a drying-oil vehicle. They may also contain various resins and special compounds to give characteristics such as gloss, scuff-resistance, etc.

There are letterpress inks which dry by penetration *(newsprint inks)*, by evaporation *(heat-set inks)*, and by precipitation *(moisture-set inks)*. Heat-set inks are formulated with high-boiling, slow-evaporating petroleum oils and solvents. These provide maximum press stability, yet dry rapidly with heat.

Offset-Lithographic Inks

Lithographic inks are formulated to print from plane surfaces, that is, from printing plates that have neither raised nor recessed image areas. Lithography is the only printing process in which chemicals and chemistry play a major part.

Lithographic inks are generally very strong in color value to compensate for the lesser amount applied. They are perhaps the strongest of all inks next to collotype inks. The average ink application is about half that of letterpress.

Basically, lithographic inks are similar to letterpress inks of the oxidizing type. However, they contain more water-resistant vehicles and pigments that do not bleed. Heat-set litho inks are also similar to their letterpress counterparts but have special requirements for vehicles and pigments as noted above. In offset lithography (as in letterpress) the resin-solvent inks are very successful due to their quick-setting on coated papers, high gloss, and resistance to emulsifying.

Letterset inks For letterset inks there are no pigment restrictions to prevent bleeding into a water fountain solution, since letterset does not require dampening mechanism. Any pigment used for letterpress may be used for letterset. Letterset inks are stronger than letterpress but not as strong as conventional offset inks.

Gravure Inks

Gravure inks are rapid-drying fluid inks which must have sufficient body to be *pulled* from the engraved wells in the cylinder or plate. They dry principally by the evaporation of the solvent in the ink, with or without the use of heat. Gravure inks must be free of hard particles that could scratch the engraved cylinder or plate.

A wide variety of solvents are used in gravure depending on the substrate. Most gravure inks are very volatile, and can cause fire if not handled properly. Solvent recovery is used in many publication plants to eliminate pollution from the evaporated solvents. Water-based inks are being developed to eliminate both the fire hazard and solvent pollution.

Flexographic Inks

Flexography, a method of rotary letterpress printing, utilizes flexible rubber plates and fast-drying fluid inks. Flexo inks are used in printing almost every kind of surface, from carpeting and wallboard to the various cellophane and plastic films, metal foils, etc. The exceptional color effects afforded by flexography are best exploited by using large masses of color. Flexo inks consist of colorants, which may be either pigments or soluble dyes, together with a vehicle or binder.

Flexo inks are either alcohol or water base. Alcohol base inks are the most common and dry by evaporation. Water base inks cost less and dry by both evaporation and absorption.

Screen Printing Inks

These inks are usually of the drying oil type, although others can be used. They have the consistency of thick paint. Inks are made in any color, using a suitable binder for the material to be printed. All inks must be short and buttery to print sharp and squeegee with little resistance. To prevent clogging of the screen, the solvents used should not evaporate too rapidly.

Solventless Inks

Two new ink systems have been developed to eliminate air pollution from conventional inks in web printing and starch anti-set-off spray in sheet-fed printing.

Catalytic inks used for web printing consist of two liquid pre-polymers like melamine and formaldehyde which crosslink to form a solid in the presence of an acid. An acid salt is incorporated with the mixture to keep them from crosslinking on the press and at ordinary temperatures. When the web goes through the drier, the acid salt is decomposed and the polymers crosslink to form a dry, solid, thermosetting resin. These inks and hybrid systems containing small amounts of inert solvent are finding use in web offset in areas where air quality regulations are being strictly enforced.

UV curing inks are another type of solventless inks which consist of liquid photopolymers with initiators which, on exposure to large doses of UV light, release free radicals which polymerize the polymer to a dry, solid, thermosetting resin. This system is being used for both sheet-fed and web. It offers the possibility of between-unit curing and the advantage of dry trapping, and some presses are so equipped. In sheet-fed printing these inks eliminate starch spray and open up the possibility of in-line operations. While between-unit curing shows some advantages in trapping, the inks seem to dry with a lower gloss. Apparently setting the film too rapidly before it has a chance to level out reduces the gloss of the final film. Also on between-unit curing, the black ink is usually printed first, followed by cyan, magenta and yellow.

Specialty Inks

High gloss inks Basically, gloss inks contain an extra quantity of varnish, giving them a glossy appearance when dry. For best results, stocks specially coated for gloss inks should be used. In general, the more resistant the paper is to penetration of the vehicle, the higher the gloss. That property of paper is generally referred to as *holdout*. When heat is used in drying, it has a tendency to reduce gloss. High gloss inks are available for both letterpress and offset.

Quick-setting inks in both letterpress and offset have been very successful on enamel and cast-coated papers. These inks are made from a resin-solvent vehicle system. Upon contact with paper the coating quickly drains the solvents, yielding a film that sets or dries for almost immediate handling. Quick-setting inks usually have a fair gloss.

Heat-set inks Considered one of the most important developments in recent years, heat-set inks are quick-drying inks. The solvents are vaporized as they pass through a heating chamber, leaving the pigment and binding resins fixed to paper in such a manner that there is no chance for spread or excessive penetration into the paper. Therefore, presses must be equipped with a heating unit and exhaust system to drive off the solvents, and chill rolls to set the heated resins.

Metallic inks Metallic powders, such as aluminum and copper alloys, mixed with the proper varnish base, give a pleasing metallic luster. The bronze powder and vehicle for preparing gold inks are mixed just before using, since the majority of gold inks tarnish rapidly after mixing. The varnish used dries rapidly and has sufficient binding qualities to bind and hold the powder to the paper surface. Coated papers give the best results. However, on a rough surface paper, a base ink is sometimes printed first, allowed to dry, and overprinted with gold. Both aluminum and gold inks can be printed letterpress, offset or gravure. When printed by offset, alkaline fountain solutions are usually used to prevent tarnishing of the bronze powder.

Moisture-set inks This letterpress ink consists of pigments dispersed in a vehicle composed of a water-insoluble binder dissolved in a water-miscible, or water-receptive solvent, usually a glycol. Upon subjecting the printing to either steam, fine mist or water, the water-miscible solvent picks up some of the water which causes the water-insoluble binder to precipitate out of solution and bind the pigment firmly to the paper. Moisture-set inks are relatively free from odor, making them ideal for food package printing.

Magnetic inks In order to increase the speed and efficiency of handling bank checks, magnetic inks were developed. These inks are made with pigments which can be magnetized after printing, and the printed characters are later "recognized" by electronic reading equipment. These inks must be formulated to produce high grade printing which will meet the rigid requirements of the reading equipment. Makeready and amount of ink must be precise and consistent.

1 2 3 4 5 6 7 8 9 0 ⑆ ⑆ ⑇ ⑈

Each of the ten numbers and four symbols shown above has a distinctive shape which can feed information to a computer, punch a tape, or do any one of a combination of things.

Scuff-resistant inks For many years ink manufacturers have been developing new inks that would be sufficiently scuff-resistant for the packaging industry. The inks required for container use must stay bright and appealing despite the shocks and scuffs of shipping and handling. Thanks to continued research, improved scuff-resistant inks are now available.

Fluorescent inks Formerly limited to screen printing, new finer grind pigments and greater pigment strength now permit colors to be printed in one impression by letterpress, lithography and gravure. Duotones and even full color process are now feasible. The naturally bright inks reflect and emit light, making use of ultraviolet light waves which other inks cannot utilize. The semi-transparency of the inks permits overprinting to achieve intermediate color tones.

Fluorescent inks must be printed on a white surface and provide maximum brilliance when contrasted with dark surrounding hues. They are suited for jobs of a semi-permanent nature, such as labeling, packaging, direct mail, etc.

Varnish and lacquer are used over printing for protection as well as gloss. The inkmaker should know that the printing will be lacquered so that he can formulate his inks to be lacquer-resistant. Otherwise, the inks are apt to bleed through the varnish or lacquer. The varnish maker must be informed as to the chemical resistances (soaps, acids, etc.), scuff tests, gloss requirements, and other general specifications required of the varnish so that the proper formulation can be selected.

A variety of press-applied varnishes is available. These are used on standard presses without heat, and the drying is by oxidation.

Special Characteristics

Inks must have other special characteristics to be satisfactory for the variety of uses to which printed matter is subjected. Inks must dry so that they are *rub* and *smudge resistant.* Labels and packaging printing must be *scuff* and *scratch resistant.* Printed matter used for window displays and outdoors requires inks that are *light fast* and *resist fading.* Ink used for soap wrappers must be *alkali resistant* and not bleed with the product. *Alcohol proofness,* or resistance to smearing by alcohol, is a must for liquor labels. Wrappers to be hot waxed must have inks that do not bleed in paraffin.

graphic arts
terms

To list all terms connected with the Graphic Arts would fill a book. Many would be too technical and of little value to anyone other than a skilled craftsman. In this section only the common terms used in advertising and printing today are defined:

absorption *In paper,* the property which causes it to take up liquids or vapors in contact with it. *In optics,* the partial suppression of light through a transparent or translucent material.

accordion fold *In binding,* a term used for two or more parallel folds which open like an accordion.

against the grain Folding or feeding paper at right angles to the grain of the paper.

agate line A standard of measurement for depth of columns of advertising space. Fourteen agate lines make one column inch.

airbrush *In artwork,* a small pressure gun shaped like a pencil that sprays watercolor pigment by means of compressed air. Used to correct and obtain tone or graduated tonal effects. *In platemaking,* used with an abrasive-like pumice to remove spots or other unwanted areas.

alterations *In composition,* changes made in the copy after it has been set in type.

antique finish A term describing the surface, usually on book and cover papers, that has a natural rough finish.

ascender That part of the letter which rises above the main body, as in "b".

backbone The back of a bound book connecting the two covers; also called *spine.*

backing up Printing the reverse side of a sheet already printed on one side. *In electrotyping,* backing a copper shell with metal to make the plate the required thickness.

back lining A paper or fabric adhering to the backbone or spine in a hard cover book.

bad break *In composition,* the setting of a hyphenated line as the first line of a page. Also, starting a page with a 'widow'.

base *In composition,* all the metal below the shoulder of a piece of type. *In letterpress,* the metal or wood block on which printing plates are mounted to make them type high.

basis weight The weight in pounds of a ream (500 sheets) of paper cut to a given standard size for that grade: 25 x 38 for book papers, 20 x 26 for cover papers, 22½ x 28½ or 22½ x 35 for bristols, 25½ x 30½ for index. E.g., 500 sheets 25 x 38 of 80-lb. coated will weigh eighty pounds.

bearers *In photoengraving,* the dead metal left on a plate to protect the printing surface when molding. *In composition,* type-high slugs locked up inside a chase to protect the printing surface when molding. *In presses,* the flat surfaces or rings at the ends of cylinders that come in contact with each other during printing (on American presses), and serve as a basis for determining packing thickness.

bimetal plate *In lithography,* a plate used for long runs in which the printing image base is copper or brass and the non-printing area is aluminum, stainless steel, or chromium.

black-and-white Originals or reproductions in single color, as distinguished from multicolor.

black printer *In color reproduction,* the black plate, made to give proper emphasis to neutral tones and detail.

blanket *In offset-lithography,* a rubber-surfaced fabric which is clamped around the cylinder, and transfers the image from plate to paper.

bleed If the printed image extends to the trim edge of the sheet or page, it is called bleed.

blind embossing A design which is stamped without gold leaf or ink, giving a bas-relief effect.

blind image *In lithography,* an image that has lost its ink receptivity.

blowup An enlargement.

blueprint *In offset-lithography and photoengraving,* a photoprint made from stripped-up negatives or positives, used as a proof to check position of image elements.

body *In inkmaking,* a term referring to the viscosity, or consistency, of an ink. E.g., an ink with too much body is stiff.

body type A type used for the main part or text of a printed piece, as distinguished from the headings.

bold-face type A name given to type that is heavier than the text type with which it is used.

bond paper A grade of writing or printing paper where strength, durability, and permanence are essential requirements; used for letterheads, business forms, etc.

book paper A general term for coated and uncoated papers. The basic size is 25 x 38.

break for color *In artwork and composition,* to separate the parts to be printed in different colors.

brightness *In photography,* light reflected by the copy. *In paper,* the reflectance or brilliance of the paper.

broadside Any printed advertising circular.

brochure A pamphlet bound in booklet form.

bronzing Printing with a sizing ink, then applying bronze powder while still wet to produce a metallic lustre.

bulk The degree of thickness of paper. *In book printing*, the number of pages per inch for a given basis weight.

calender rolls A set or stack of horizontal cast-iron rolls at the end of a paper machine. The paper is passed between the rolls to increase the smoothness and gloss of its surface.

caliper The thickness of paper, usually expressed in thousandths of an inch (mils).

caps and small caps Two sizes of capital letters made in one size of type, commonly used in most roman type faces.

case *In bookbinding*, the covers of a hard-bound book.

cast coated Coated paper dried under pressure against a polished cylinder to produce a high-gloss enamel finish.

catching up *In lithography*, a term which indicates that the non-image areas of a press plate are taking ink or scumming.

chalking *In printing*, a term which refers to improper drying of ink. Pigment dusts off because the vehicle has been absorbed too rapidly into the paper.

chase A rectangular metal frame in which type and plates are locked up for letterpress printing.

circular screen A circular-shaped halftone screen which enables the camera operator to obtain proper screen angles for color halftones without disturbing the copy.

coated paper Paper having a surface coating which produces a smooth finish. Surfaces vary from eggshell to glossy.

cold color *In printing*, a color which is on the bluish side.

cold type *See strike-on composition.*

collate *In binding*, the gathering of sheets or signatures.

color correction Any method such as masking, dot-etching, re-etching, and scanning, used to improve color rendition.

color filter A sheet of dyed glass, gelatin, plastic or dyed gelatin cemented between glass plates, used in photography to absorb certain colors and permit better rendition of others. The filters used for color separation are: blue, green and red.

color proofs *See progressive proofs.*

color separation *In photography*, the process of separating full color originals into the primary printing colors in negative or positive form. *In lithographic platemaking,* the manual separation of colors by handwork performed directly on the printing surface. An artist can pre-separate by using separate overlays for each color.

combination plate *In photoengraving,* halftone and line work combined on one plate; etched for both halftone and line depth.

composing stick *In composition,* a hand tool in which type is assembled and justified.

computerized composition Unjustified tape is produced on a keyboard and subsequently run through a computer which makes line-end, hyphenation and other typographic decisions. Sometimes, a computer-produced second tape is then used as input for phototypesetting (or linecasting) equipment.

condensed type A narrow or slender type face.

contact print A photographic print made from a negative or positive in contact with sensitized paper, film, or printing plate.

contact screen A photographically-made halftone screen on film having a dot structure of graded density, used in vacuum contact with the photographic film.

continuous tone A photographic image which has not been screened and contains gradient tones from black to white.

contrast The tonal gradation between highlights and shadows in an original or reproduction.

copy Any furnished material (typewritten manuscript, pictures, artwork, etc.) to be used in the production of printing.

copyboard A frame that holds original copy while it is being photographed on the camera.

copyfitting *In composition,* to determine the amount of manuscript copy that can fit into a given area for a specified size and style of type.

copy preparation *In photomechanical processes,* directions as to desired size and other details for illustrations, and the arrangement into proper position of various parts of the page to be photographed for reproduction. *In typesetting,* checking manuscript copy to insure a minimum of changes after type is set.

cover paper A general term applied to a great variety of papers used for the outside covers of catalogs, brochures, booklets, and similar pieces.

creep *In offset,* the forward movement of a blanket during printing. Can also apply to the movement of the packing under the plate or blanket during printing.

crop To eliminate portions of the copy, usually on a photograph or plate, indicated on the original by "cropmarks".

crossline screen (glass screen) *In halftone photography,* a grid pattern with opaque lines crossing each other at right angles, thus forming transparent squares or "screen apertures."

crossmarks Register marks for accurate positioning of images in step-and-repeat, double or multicolor printing; also in superimposing overlays onto a base or on each other.

curl *In paper,* the distortion of a sheet due to differences in structure or coatings from one side to the other, or to absorption of moisture on an offset press. The curl side is the concave side of the sheet.

curved plate *In letterpress,* an electrotype or stereotype which is precurved to fit the cylinder of a rotary press.

cut *In letterpress,* a photoengraving of any kind.

cut-off *In web printing,* the cut or print length corresponding to the circumference of the plate cylinder.

cutscore *In die-cutting,* a sharp-edged knife, usually several thousandths of an inch lower than the cutting rules in a die, made to cut part way into the paper or board for folding purposes.

cylinder gap *In printing presses,* the gap or space in the cylinders of a press where the mechanism for plate (or blanket) clamps and grippers is housed.

dampeners *In lithography,* cloth-covered, parchment paper or rubber (bare back) rollers that distribute the dampening solution to the press plate.

dandy roll *In papermaking,* a wire cylinder on papermaking machines that makes wove or laid effects on the texture, as well as the watermark itself. Used in the manufacture of better grades of business and book papers.

deckle *In papermaking,* the width of the wet sheet as it comes off the wire of a paper machine.

deckle edge The untrimmed feathery edges of paper formed where the pulp flows against the deckle.

deep-etch *In offset-lithography,* a positive-working plate used for long runs where the inked areas are slightly recessed below the surface.

densitometer *In photography,* a sensitive photoelectric instrument which measures the density of photographic images, or of colors. *In printing,* a reflection densitometer is used to measure the density of color to determine whether it is consistent throughout the run.

density A measure of the relative blackening of photographic images.

dermatitis *In lithography,* a skin disease, characterized by an itching rash or swelling; caused by photographic developers, chromium compounds and solvents.

descender That part of the letter which extends below the main body, as in "p".

desensitizer *In lithographic platemaking,* making non-image areas of a plate non-receptive to ink through chemical treatment of the metal. Its main ingredient is usually a gum, like gum arabic. *In photography,* an agent for decreasing color sensitivity of photographic emulsion to facilitate development under comparatively bright light.

developer *In photography,* the chemical agent and process used to render photographic images visible after exposure to light. *In lithographic platemaking,* the material used to remove the unexposed coating.

diazo *In offset platemaking,* a coating used on presensitized and wipe-on plates.

die-cutting The use of sharp steel rules to cut special shapes, like labels, boxes and containers, from printed sheets. Die-cutting can be done on either flat-bed or rotary presses. Rotary die-cutting is usually done inline with the printing.

die-stamping An intaglio process for the production of letterheads, cards, etc., printing from lettering or other designs engraved into copper or steel.

dimensional stability Ability to maintain size; resistance of paper or film to dimensional change with change in moisture content or relative humidity.

direct screen halftone *In color separation,* a halftone negative made by direct exposure on an enlarger or by contact through a halftone screen.

display type *In composition,* type set larger than the text, used to attract attention.

distributing rollers Rubber covered rollers which convey ink from the fountain onto the ink drum of a printing press.

doctor blade *In gravure,* a knife-edge blade pressed against the engraved printing cylinder which wipes away the excess ink from the non-printing areas.

dot The individual element of a halftone.

dot spread *In printing,* a defect in which dots print larger than they should, causing darker tones or colors.

double dot halftone *In lithography,* two halftone negatives combined into one printing plate, having greater tonal range than a conventional halftone. One negative reproduces the highlights and shadows; the other reproduces middletones. This should not be confused with duotones, or printing with two black plates.

draw-down *In inkmaking,* a term used to describe ink chemist's method of roughly determining color shade. A small glob of ink is placed on paper and drawn down with the edge of a putty knife spatula to get a thin film of ink.

drier *In inkmaking,* any substance added to hasten drying.

drop-out Portions of originals that do not reproduce, especially colored lines or background areas (often on purpose).

ductor roller *In lithography,* the roller in both inking and dampening mechanisms on a press which alternately contacts fountain roller and vibrating drum roller.

dummy A preliminary layout showing the position of illustrations and text as they are to appear in the final reproduction. A set of blank pages made up in advance to show the size, shape, form and general style of a piece of printing.

duotone *In photomechanics,* a term for a two-color halftone reproduction from a one-color photograph.

duplex paper Paper having a different color or finish on each side.

duplicating film A special color film used for making duplicates of color transparencies to size, so they can be stripped together and color separated as a unit.

duplicator paper A smooth, hard-surfaced paper made for use on spirit duplicators.

electrophotography Image transfer systems used in copiers to produce images using electrostatic forces. Electrofax uses a zinc oxide coating; Xerography uses a selenium surface.

em *In composition,* the square of a type body. So named because the letter "M" in early fonts was usually cast on a square body.

embossed finish Paper with a raised or depressed surface resembling wood, cloth, leather or other pattern.

embossing Impressing an image in relief to achieve a raised surface; either over printing, or on blank paper (which is called blind embossing).

en One-half the width of an em.

enamel A term applied to a coated paper or to a coating material on a paper.

english finish A grade of book paper with a smoother, more uniform surface than machine finish.

etch *In photoengraving,* to produce an image on a plate by chemical or electrolytic action. *In offset-lithography,* an acidified gum solution used to desensitize the non-printing areas of the plate; also, an acid solution added to the fountain water to help keep non-printing areas of the plate free from ink.

extended type A type whose width is greater than normal.

face The printing surface of a piece of type.

facsimile The exact reproduction of a letter, document or signature. Sometimes abbreviated as "facsim" or "fax".

facsimile transmission The process of scanning graphic material to convert the image into electric signals which may be transmitted to produce a recorded likeness of the original.

feeder The section of a press which separates the sheets and feeds them in position for printing.

felt side The smoother side of the paper for printing. The top side of the sheet in paper manufacturing.

filling in (or filling up) *In letterpress or offset-lithography,* a condition where ink fills the area between the halftone dots or plugs up the type.

filter *In color separation photography,* a colored piece of gelatin used over or between the lens. *(See color filter.)*

fixing Chemical action following development to remove unexposed silver halide, to make the image stable and insensitive to further exposure.

flash exposure *In halftone photography,* the supplementary exposure given to strengthen the dots in the shadow areas of negatives.

flat *In offset-lithography,* the assembled composite of negatives or positives, ready for platemaking. Also, a picture that is lacking in contrast.

flat etching The chemical reduction of the silver deposit in a continuous-tone or halftone plate, brought about by placing it in a tray containing an etching solution.

flow *In printing,* the ability of an ink to spread over the surface of the rollers of a press.

flush cover A cover that has been trimmed the same size as the inside text pages.

flush left (or right) *In composition,* type set to line up at the left (or right). This page is set flush left *and* right.

flush paragraph A paragraph with no indention.

flying paster *In web printing,* an automatic pasting device that splices a new web of paper onto an expiring roll, without stopping the press.

fog *In photography,* density in the non-image areas.

folio The page number.

font *In composition,* the complete assortment of type of one size and face.

form Type and other matter locked in a chase for printing.

form rollers The rollers, either inking or dampening, which directly contact the plate on a printing press.

format The size, style, type page, margins, printing requirements, etc., of a printed piece.

fountain solution *In lithography,* a solution of water, gum arabic and other chemicals used to dampen the plate and keep non-printing areas from accepting ink.

free sheet Paper free of mechanical wood pulp.

"f" stops Fixed sizes for setting lens apertures.

furniture *In lockup,* wood or metal blocks used to fill the blank spaces in a form.

fuzz Fibers projecting from the surface of a sheet of paper.

galley A shallow metal tray used to hold type.

galley proof A proof taken of type standing in a galley, before being made up into pages.

gamma A measure of contrast in photographic images.

gathering The assembling of folded signatures in proper sequence.

gear streaks *In printing,* parallel streaks appearing across the printed sheet at same interval as gear teeth on the cylinder.

generation Each succeeding stage in reproduction from the original copy.

goldenrod paper *In offset-lithography,* a specially coated masking paper of yellow or orange color used by strippers to assemble and position negatives for exposure onto plates.

grain *In papermaking,* the direction in which most fibers lie which corresponds with the direction the paper is made on paper machine.

graining *In lithography,* subjecting the surface of metal plates to the action of abrasives. Greater water-retention and adhesion of coating is imparted to an otherwise non-porous surface.

gray scale A strip of standard gray tones, ranging from white to black, placed at the side of original copy during photography to measure tonal range and contrast (gamma) obtained.

grippers *In printing presses,* metal fingers that clamp on paper and control its flow as it passes through.

gripper edge The leading edge of paper as it passes through a printing press. Also, the front edge of a lithographic or wrap-around plate that is secured to front clamp of plate cylinder.

gripper margin Unprintable blank edge of paper on which grippers bear, usually ½ inch or less.

groundwood pulp A mechanically-prepared wood pulp used in the manufacture of newsprint and publication papers.

gum arabic *In offset-lithography,* used in platemaking and on press to desensitize the non-printing areas of plates, and with bichromate to sensitize deep-etch and bimetal plates.

gutter The blank space or inner margin, from printing area to binding.

halation *In photography,* a blurred effect, resembling a halo, usually occurring in highlight areas or around bright objects.

halftone The reproduction of continuous tone artwork, such as a photograph, through a crossline or contact screen, which converts the image into dots of various sizes.

hard copy *In phototypesetting,* typewritten copy on ordinary paper produced simultaneously with magnetic or paper tape on most keyboards.

hard dot *See soft dot.*

head margin The white space above first line on a page.

hickeys *In offset-lithography,* spots or imperfections in the printing due to such things as dirt on the press, dried ink skin, paper particles, etc.

highlight The lightest or whitest parts in a photograph represented in a halftone reproduction by the smallest dots or the absence of all dots.

hot metal composition Cast metal type set either by hand or in a linecasting machine.

hydrophilic Water-loving; preferring to be wet by water.

hydrophobic Water-hating; water repellent.

hypo An abbreviation for sodium thiosulfate, or sodium hyposulfite, a chemical used to fix the image on a photographic film after it has been developed.

idiot tape *In computerized phototypesetting,* raw, unhyphenated, unjustified paper or magnetic tape.

imposition The laying out of pages in a press form so that they will be in the correct order after the printed sheet is folded.

impression *In printing,* the pressure of type, plate or blanket as it comes in contact with the paper.

ink fountain *In printing presses,* the device which stores and supplies ink to the inking rollers.

insert A printed piece prepared for insertion into a publication or another printed piece.

italic The style of letters that slope forward, in distinction from upright, or roman, letters. Used for words requiring emphasis.

jog To align sheets of paper into a compact pile.

justify *In composition,* to space out lines uniformly to the correct length.

kerning *In typesetting,* adjusting the spacing between two characters closer, so that part of their letter shapes overhang.

key To code copy to a dummy by means of symbols, usually letters. Insertions are sometimes "keyed" in like manner. *In lockup,* a device for operating quoins.

keyboard *In phototypesetting,* the input mechanism which records onto paper or magnetic tape. It is usually separate from the typesetting unit, but sometimes is directly attached to it.

keyline *In artwork,* an outline drawing on finished art to indicate the exact shape, position, and size for such elements as halftones, line sketches, etc.

key plate *In color printing,* the plate used as a guide for the register of other colors. It normally contains the most detail.

kraft A paper or board made from unbleached woodpulp (brown in color) by the sulfate process.

lacquer A clear coating, usually glossy, applied to a printed sheet for protection or appearance.

laid paper Paper with a pattern of parallel lines at equal distances, giving a ribbed effect.

lamination A plastic film bonded by heat and pressure to a printed sheet for protection or appearance.

layout The drawing or sketch of a proposed printed piece. *In platemaking*, a sheet indicating the settings for the step-and-repeat machine.

lead *In composition*, a thin strip of metal used for spacing between lines of type.

leaders *In composition*, rows of dashes or dots used to guide the eye across the page. Used in tabular work, programs, tables of contents, etc.

ledger paper A grade of business paper generally used for keeping records. It is subjected to appreciable wear and requires a high degree of durability and permanence.

letterset (dry offset) The printing process which uses a blanket (like conventional offset) for transferring the image from plate to paper. Unlike lithography, it uses a relief plate and requires no dampening system.

letterspacing The placing of additional space between each letter of a word.

line copy Any copy suitable for reproduction without using a halftone screen.

lockup *In letterpress*, to position a form in a chase for printing.

logotype (or logo) The name of a company or product in a special design used as a trademark in advertising.

long ink An ink that has good flow on ink rollers of a press. If the ink is too long, it breaks up into filaments on the press, and causes "flying" as on a newspaper press.

lower case The small letters in type, as distinguished from the capital letters.

M Abbreviation for a quantity of 1000.

machine coated Paper which is coated one or two sides on the paper machine.

makeready *In letterpress*, the building up of the press form so that heavy and light areas print with the correct impression.

makeup *In composition*, the arrangement of lines of type and illustrations into pages or sections of proper length.

mask *In color separation photography*, an intermediate photographic negative or positive used in color correction. *In offset-lithography*, opaque material used to protect open or selected areas of a printing plate during exposure.

master A plate for a duplicating machine.

matrix A mold in which type is cast in linecasting machines. *In stereotyping,* the paper mold or mat made from a type form.

matte finish Dull paper finish without gloss or luster.

matte print Photoprint having a dull finish.

measure *In composition,* the width of type, usually expressed in picas.

mechanical *Used mostly in offset,* a term for a camera-ready pasteup of artwork. It includes type, photos, line art, etc., all on one piece of artboard.

middletones The tonal range between highlights and shadows of a photograph or reproduction.

mimeograph paper A paper with the toothy, absorbent surface required for mimeographing.

moiré *In color process printing,* the undesirable screen pattern caused by incorrect screen angles of halftones.

molleton *In offset-lithography,* a thick cotton fabric similar to flannel used on the dampening rollers of a press.

montage *In artwork,* several photographs pasted to one artboard in a pleasing manner. They can be placed on angles, overlapped, cut to various shapes, etc.

mottle The spotty or uneven appearance of printing. Most pronounced in solid areas.

mullen tester A machine for testing the bursting strength of paper.

Mylar *In offset preparation,* a polyester film made by Du Pont specially suited for stripping positives because of its mechanical strength and dimensional stability.

negative *In photography,* film containing an image in which the values of the original are reversed so that the dark areas appear light and vice versa. *(See positive.)*

newsprint Paper made mostly from groundwood pulp and small amounts of chemical pulp; used for printing newspapers.

oblong *In binding,* a booklet or catalog bound on the shorter dimension.

offset *See set-off.*

opacity That property of paper which minimizes the "show-through" of printing from the back side or the next sheet.

opaque *In photoengraving and offset-lithography,* to paint out areas on a negative not wanted on the plate. *In paper,* the property which makes it less transparent.

opaque ink An ink that conceals all color beneath it.

orthochromatic Photographic surfaces insensitive to red but sensitive to ultraviolet, blue, green, and yellow rays.

overhang cover A cover larger in size than the pages it encloses.

overlay *In artwork*, a transparent covering over copy where color break, instructions or corrections are marked. Also, transparent or translucent prints which, when placed one on the other, form a composite picture.

overprinting Double printing; printing over an area that already has been printed.

overrun *In printing*, copies printed in excess of the specified quantity.

overset *In composition*, type set in excess of space needs in publications, etc.

packing *In printing presses*, paper used to underlay the image or impression cylinder in letterpress, or the plate or blanket in lithography, to get proper squeeze or pressure for printing.

panchromatic Photographic film sensitive to all visible colors.

paper master A paper printing plate used on an offset-duplicator. The image is made by hand drawing, typewriter or electrophotography.

paste drier *In inkmaking*, a type of drier used in inks, usually a combination of drying compounds.

pasteup *See mechanical.*

patent base *In letterpress*, a slotted metal base on which unmounted electrotypes are secured for printing.

pebbling A process of embossing paper after printing to give a uniform ripple or pebbled effect.

perfecting press A printing press that prints both sides of the paper in one pass.

pH A number used for expressing the acidity or alkalinity of solutions. A value of 7 is neutral in a scale ranging from 0 to 14. Solutions of a lower value are considered acid while those higher are alkaline.

photomechanical Pertaining to any platemaking process using photographic negatives or positives exposed onto plates or cylinders covered with photosensitive coatings.

pi Type mixed, and in an unusable condition.

pica Printer's unit of measurement used principally in measuring lines. One pica equals approximately 1/6 of an inch.

picking The lifting of the paper surface during printing. It occurs when pulling force (tack) of ink is greater than surface strength of paper.

pigment *In printing inks,* the fine solid particles used to give color, body or opacity.

piling *In printing,* the building up or caking of ink on rollers, plate or blanket; will not transfer readily. Also, the accumulation of paper coating on the blanket of offset press.

pin register The use of accurately positioned holes and special pins on copy, film, plates and presses to insure proper register or fit of colors.

plate finish A smooth, hard finish of paper achieved by calendering.

point Printer's unit of measurement, used principally for designating type sizes. There are 12 points to a pica; approximately 72 points to an inch.

porosity The property of paper that allows the permeation of air, an important factor in ink penetration.

positive *In photography,* film containing an image in which the dark and light values are the same as the original. The reverse of negative.

pre-press proofs Proofs made by photographic techniques to eliminate the expense of making press proofs.

presensitized plate *In photomechanics,* a metal or paper plate that has been precoated with a light-sensitive coating.

press proofs *In color reproduction,* a proof of a color subject on a printing press, in advance of the production run.

pressure-sensitive paper Material with an adhesive coating, protected by a backing sheet until used, which will stick without moistening.

primary colors *In printing inks,* yellow, magenta (process red) and cyan (process blue). *In light,* red, green and blue.

process lens A highly corrected photographic lens for line, halftone and color photography.

process printing The printing from a series of two or more halftone plates to produce intermediate colors and shades. In four-color process: yellow, magenta, cyan, and black.

progressive proofs (progs) Proofs made from the separate plates in color process work, showing the sequence of printing and the result after each additional color has been applied.

psychrometer A wet-and-dry bulb type of hygrometer. Considered the most accurate of the instruments practical for industrial plant use for determining relative humidity.

quad *In composition,* blank spacing material less than type high used to fill out lines.

quality control *In printing,* the process of taking random samples during the run to check the consistency of quality.

quoin *In letterpress,* a steel wedge-shaped or expanding device used in lockup.

ream Five hundred sheets of paper.

reducers *In printing inks,* varnishes, solvents, oily or greasy compounds used to reduce the consistency for printing. *In photography,* chemicals used to reduce the size of halftone dots or the density of negative or positive images.

reflection copy *In photography,* illustrative copy that is viewed and must be photographed by light reflected from its surface. Examples are photographs, dye-transfer prints, etc.

register *In printing,* fitting of two or more printing images on the same paper in exact alignment with each other.

register marks Crosses or other devices applied to original copy prior to photography. Used for positioning negatives in register, or for register of two or more colors in process printing.

relative humidity (RH) The amount of water vapor present in the atmosphere expressed as a percentage of the maximum that could be present at the *same* temperature.

reproduction proof *In composition,* the proof of a type form for purposes of photographic reproduction.

right-angle fold *In binding,* a term used for two or more folds that are at 90° angles to each other.

roller stripping *In lithography,* a term denoting that the ink does not adhere to the metal ink rollers on a press.

routing *In letterpress,* the cutting away of the non-printing areas of a plate.

rub-proof *In printing,* an ink that has reached maximum dryness and does not mar with normal abrasion.

run-around *In composition,* the term describing a type area set in measures that are adjusted to fit around a picture or another element of the design.

running head A title repeated at the top of each page of a book.

saddle wire *In binding*, to fasten a booklet by wiring it through the middle fold of the sheets.

safelight *In photography*, the special darkroom lamp used for illumination without fogging sensitized materials.

scaling Determining the proper size of an image to be reduced or enlarged.

scanner An electronic device used in the making of color separations.

score To impress or indent a mark with a string or rule in the paper to make folding easier.

screen *See contact screen and crossline screen.*

screen angles *In color reproduction*, the angle to which the halftone screen is placed with relation to one another, to avoid the formation of an undesirable moiré pattern. A set of angles often used are: black 45°, magenta 75°, yellow 90°, cyan 105°.

screen ruling The number of lines or dots per inch on a contact screen or ruled glass halftone (crossline) screen.

screened print *In photography*, a print made from a halftone negative.

scum *In offset-lithography*, a film of ink printing in the non-image areas of a plate where it should not print.

self cover A cover of the same paper as inside text pages.

serif The short cross-lines at the ends of the main strokes of many letters in some type faces.

set-off *In presswork*, when the ink of a printed sheet rubs off or marks the next sheet as it is being delivered. Also called *offset.*

shadow The darkest parts in a photograph, represented in a halftone by the largest dots.

sharpen To decrease in strength, as when halftone dots become smaller; opposite of "thicken" or "dot spread".

sheetwise To print one side of a sheet of paper with one form or plate, then turn the sheet over and print the other side with another form using same gripper and side guide.

short ink An ink that is buttery and does not flow freely.

show-through *In printing*, the undesirable condition in which the printing on the reverse side of a sheet can be seen through the sheet under normal lighting conditions.

side wire *In binding*, to wire the sheets or signatures of a magazine or booklet on the side near the backbone.

signature *In web printing and binding*, the name given to a printed sheet after it has been folded.

sizing The treatment of paper which gives it resistance to the penetration of liquids (particularly water) or vapors.

skid A platform support for a pile of cut sheets.

slitting Cutting printed sheets or webs into two or more sections by means of cutting wheels on a press or folder.

slug *In composition,* a one-piece line of type. Also, a strip of metal, usually 6 points, used for spacing between lines.

small caps An alphabet of SMALL CAPITAL LETTERS available in most roman type faces approximately the size of the lower case letters. Used in combination with larger capital letters.

soft dot *In photography,* a dot is called 'soft' when the halation or fringe around the dot is excessive and almost equals the area of the dot itself. Conversely, when the fringe is so slight as to be barely noticeable and the dot is very sharp, it is called 'hard'.

soft ink Descriptive of consistency of lithographic inks.

spine *See backbone.*

spiral binding A book bound with wires in spiral form inserted through holes punched along the binding side.

staging *See stopping out.*

static neutralizer *In printing presses,* an attachment designed to remove the static electricity from the paper to avoid ink set-off and trouble with feeding the paper.

step-and-repeat *In photomechanics,* the procedure of multiple exposure using the same image by *stepping* it in position according to a predetermined layout.

stet A proofreader's mark, written in the margin, signifying that copy marked for corrections should remain as it was.

stock Paper or other material to be printed.

stopping out *In photomechanics,* application of opaque to photographic negatives; application of special lacquer to protect areas in positives in dot etching; staging of halftone plates during relief etching; protecting certain areas of deep-etched plates so that no ink will be deposited on the protected areas.

stream feeder *In printing presses,* a type of feeder that feeds several sheets overlapping each other toward the grippers.

strike-on composition Type set by a direct-impression method, or on typewriter composing machines. Also known as cold type.

strike-through *See show-through.*

stripping *In offset-lithography,* the positioning of negatives (or positives) on a flat (goldenrod) prior to platemaking.

substance The weight in pounds of a ream (500 sheets) of paper cut to the standard size (17 x 22) for business papers (bond, ledger, mimeograph, duplicator and manifold). E.g., 20 pounds. Similar to basis weight of other grades of paper.

sulphate pulp Paper pulp made from wood chips cooked under pressure in a solution of caustic soda and sodium sulphide. Known as kraft.

sulphite pulp Paper pulp made from wood chips cooked under pressure in a solution of bisulphite of lime.

supercalender *In papermaking,* a calender stack, separate from the papermaking machine, with alternate metal and resilient rolls, used to produce a high finish on paper.

surprint *In photomechanics,* exposure from a second negative superimposed upon a previously exposed image of the first negative.

tack *In printing inks,* the property of cohesion between particles; the pulling power or separation force of ink. A *tacky* ink has high separation forces and can cause picking or splitting of weak papers.

text The body matter of a page or book, as distinguished from the headings.

thirty Used in newspapers, the symbol "—30—" means the end of the story.

tints Various even tone areas (strengths) of a solid color.

tissue overlay A thin, translucent paper placed over artwork for protection; used to indicate color break and corrections.

tooth A characteristic of paper, a slightly rough finish, which permits it to take ink readily.

transparent *See show-through.*

transparent copy *In photography,* illustrative copy such as a color transparency or color negative through which light must pass in order for it to be seen.

transparent ink A printing ink which does not conceal the color beneath. A transparent ink allows the undercolors to show through. Process inks are transparent so that they will blend to form other colors.

transpose To exchange the position of a letter, word, or line with another letter, word, or line.

trapping The ability of an already printed ink film to accept a succeeding or overprinted ink film.

trim marks *In printing*, marks placed on the copy to indicate the edge of the page.

two-sheet detector *In printing presses*, a device for stopping the press when more than one sheet attempts to feed into the grippers.

type gauge *In composition*, a printer's tool calibrated in picas used for type measurement.

type high 0.918 inch; the standard in letterpress.

undercut *In printing presses*, the difference between the radius of the cylinder bearers and the cylinder body, to allow for plate (or blanket) and packing thickness.

-up *In printing*, two-up, three-up, etc., refers to imposition of material to be printed on a larger size sheet to take advantage of full press capacity.

vacuum frame *In platemaking*, a vacuum device for holding copy and reproduction material in contact during exposure.

varnish A thin, protective coating applied to a printed sheet for protection or appearance. *Also, in inkmaking*, it can be all or part of the ink vehicle.

vehicle *In printing inks*, the fluid component which acts as a carrier for the pigment.

vellum finish *In papermaking*, a toothy finish which is relatively absorbent for fast ink penetration.

vignette An illustration in which the background fades gradually away until it blends into the unprinted paper.

viscosity *In printing inks*, a broad term encompassing the properties of tack and flow.

walk-off *In lithography*, the failure of part of an image to adhere to the metal plate during printing.

warm color *In printing*, a color which is on the reddish side.

washup The process of cleaning the rollers, form or plate, and sometimes the ink fountain of a press.

watermark *In papermaking*, a design impressed on paper by the raised pattern of the dandy roll during manufacture.

wax engraving *In letterpress platemaking*, a method of engraving or impressing lines or type in wax, thereby creating a mold which can be electrotyped. Used for ruled forms.

web A roll of paper used in web or rotary printing.

web press A press which prints from rolls (or webs) of paper.

web tension The amount of pull or tension applied in the direction of travel of a web of paper by the action of a web-fed press.

widow *In composition,* a single word in a line by itself, ending a paragraph; frowned upon in good typography.

wipe-on plate *In offset-lithography,* a plate on which a light-sensitive coating is wiped on or applied with a coating machine.

wire-o binding A continuous double series of wire loops run through punched slots along the binding side of a booklet.

wire side *In papermaking,* the side of a sheet next to the wire in manufacturing; opposite from felt or top side.

with the grain Folding or feeding paper parallel to the grain of the paper.

woodcut An illustration in lines of varying thickness, cut in relief on plank-grain wood, for the purpose of making prints.

work and tumble To print one side of a sheet of paper, then turn the sheet over from gripper to back using the same side guide and plate to print the second side.

work and turn To print one side of a sheet of paper, then turn the sheet over from left to right and print the second side. The same gripper and plate is used for printing both sides.

wove paper Paper having a uniform unlined surface and a soft smooth finish.

wraparound plate *In rotary letterpress,* a thin one-piece relief plate which is wrapped around the press cylinder like an offset plate. Can be used for direct or indirect (offset) printing.

wrinkles Creases in paper occurring during printing. *In inks,* the uneven surface formed during drying.

wrong font *In proofreading,* the mark "WF" indicates a letter or figure of the wrong size or face.

xerography A copying process that utilizes a selenium surface and electrostatic forces to form an image. *(See electro-photography.)*

IP printing
papers

International Paper Company, founded in 1898, today employs over 51,000 men and women in pulp and paper mills and converting plants in the United States, Canada and overseas. Behind these mills and plants is a large woodlands organization which operates the company's forest holdings according to the latest standards of scientific forest management and under the principles of multiple use.

International Paper's numerous and diversified paper products are known and used throughout the world. The fine printing papers, described on the following pages, are distributed nationally by leading paper merchants.

BUSINESS PAPERS

International® Business Paper is an all-purpose premium watermarked business paper, combining high brightness and the crisp feel one expects in a prestige number one line. International Business Paper can be used in all four major processes of multilith, duplicator, mimeograph and xerographic. It has excellent dimensional stability and can be embossed or engraved to provide truly distinctive letterheads. This grade is produced to exacting quality standards assuring trouble-free runnability on all high speed office equipment. White only.

Springhill® Business Paper is a premium #4 multipurpose bond and is listed as such in the Competitive Gradefinder. It can be used for efficient volume work on the four major office reproduction processes: multilith, duplicator, mimeograph and xerographic. Eliminates need for stocking different kinds of business papers. Springhill Business Paper feeds and delivers smoothly, and consistently produces uniformly sharp repetitive copies. Its whiteness, opacity and stiffness make it ideal for letterheads, newsletters, bulletins, price schedules, etc. Available in white and six attractive colors.

IPCO® Business Paper is a standard #4 multipurpose bond and is listed as such in the Competitive Gradefinder. It has lower brightness and opacity than Springhill Business Paper. It features the functional characteristics of the Springhill sheet and can be used when high brightness and opacity are not required.

IPCO® Bond/Mimeo, Duplicator and Xerographic are all standard #4 papers and are listed as such in the Competitive Gradefinder. These sheets are produced for those customers who may require a specifically tailored sheet for a particular piece of reproduction equipment.

Springhill® and IPCO® High Speed Copy Paper is a sheet specifically designed for maximum performance on modern high speed copying duplicators.

BOARD GRADES

Springhill® White Tag is the workhorse of the Springhill board grade family and has been acknowledged as the leader in the field. Its soft suede finish provides excellent printability with faster ink drying time. Consequently, Springhill White Tag is suitable for many end uses from tags to menus, and from tent cards to direct mail pieces.

Springhill® Manila Tag is another time-proven member of the Springhill line. Its consistent shade coupled with toughness, levelness and printability make it suitable for a variety of uses such as tags, job tickets, heavy duty envelopes, file folders, forms, etc.

Springhill® Colored Tag. A leader in its field, this versatile tag board has many uses—tickets, menus, catalog inserts, dividers, folders, etc. Excellent snap, strength and appearance—economical too, in cost and printing performance by letterpress, offset or silk screen. Available in six colors.

Springhill® Index. Truly a versatile board grade with unusual printability for an index. Noted for its durability, strength, snap and resilience, it is a smart choice for functional printed pieces requiring frequency of use and abuse. Its high brightness and soft, surface-sized finish provide exceptional printing results with offset lithography, letterpress or silk screen. Ideal for index systems, file cards, case records, menus, charts, ruled forms, die-cut displays, sales kits, manual and catalog covers and dividers, direct mail. Available in white and six colors.

Springhill® Vellum Bristol, with its stiffness and toothy finish, endows any printed piece with a textured warmth and graphic personality. Available in popular sizes in white and six colors: canary, blue, roman gold, pink, green and ivory. The marvelous ink receptivity, holdout and affinity of Springhill Vellum Bristol permit matched or process inks to print with easy confidence for beautiful reproductions. The designer shades are compatible partners for creative three or four multi-color effects with the use of one or two ink combinations and color tint percents. Its physical properties of die-cutting, embossing, scoring and folding are unsurpassed. Ideal for a host of printing end uses such as greeting and mailing cards, catalog and annual report covers, tent and car cards, posters, calendars, folders, brochures, direct mail and promotional pieces.

Feedcote® offers a quality and economic choice between expensive enamels and uncoated bristols. A double blade coated surface insures superior ink and varnish holdout permitting quality printing with reduced ink consumption. A quality coating applied on a durable bleached board provides a stable, easy-to-print stock especially suitable for promotional folders, point-of-purchase displays, tent cards, company and annual report covers, and direct response advertising.

ADVERTISING AND PUBLICATION PAPERS

Bookmark® is a premium book paper specifically designed and developed for textbook and tradebook publishers' needs. This free sheet paper has the limp, soft feel that good book papers should have. Pages turn easily and then relax no matter what binding is used. This fine publication grade is made to N.A.S.T.A. specifications and comes in three shades: natural cream, standard white, and blue white. Surfaces available in each weight are antique, eggshell, standard and English finish.

Springhill® Book is our best value in a bulking book sheet. It is an adaptation of our well-known uncoated offset grade. It is made as a book printer would want it, carefully produced to four bulk levels in each weight (high bulk, vellum, wove and smooth) and in our popular 555 cream shade as well as standard 110 white. This is the lowest cost alternative for those jobs that do not require N.A.S.T.A. opacity levels, but still must fit the other needs of the book publisher and manufacturer.

Springhill® Offset is a particular favorite with printers because quality printing can be done at low cost. Its high brightness gives excellent contrast for text copy, and its hardwood furnish provides good bulk and opacity. Available in wove and vellum finish in a variety of sizes and weights, which include the .006" (65 lb.) minimum caliper required for postcard stock.

Springhill® Vellum Offset Colors ideally lend themselves to creative design and imaginative printing with seven warm pastel shades of ivory, sand, mist green, canary, blue, green and pink which are available in 50, 60 and 70 lb. basis weights. Their easy-going color personalities are compatible for multicolor effects when only one or two printing inks are used. Color-on-color executions become a practical reality when paper color can substitute a printing ink to hold production costs down. Available in popular stock sizes, the distinctive vellum finish adds richness and depth to any printed piece. It is a favorite choice for folders, inserts, circulars, broadsides, tip-ons, forms, promotional and direct mail pieces.

Educator® is a coated groundwood (unsupered) book paper. Good printability, and brightness with additional characteristics such as fine texture, feel, good ink holdout and dependable printability make Educator an ideal book publishing grade.

International Coated Litho® C1S is an exceptional value in label, commercial printing and converting end uses such as record and book jackets and box wraps. Its smooth, level coating provides excellent ink and varnish holdout, while the proper fiber blend gives it outstanding press room performance. Available in 60, 70 and 80 lb. basis. International Coated Litho C1S offers a wide range of possibilities to the value-conscious printer and designer.

Bookmark Endleaf™ is a strong, rugged sheet for the most demanding use in bookbinding. Bookmark Endleaf exceeds the standards established by N.A.S.T.A. Its fold endurance and bright white finish provide the performance as well as the appearance the book publisher wants. Designed to be readily glued, it also is suitable for offset or letterpress printing.

Publication Papers

Publication Gloss® is a coated groundwood paper suitable for letterpress and rotogravure printing. The sheet is designed for a smooth surface and superior ink hold-out besides providing the economies necessary for magazine and catalog printing. Its good runnability means trouble-free pressruns.

Hudson® Web Gloss is a coated groundwood paper suitable for offset printing. The combination of superior runnability and ink hold-out plus resistance to water and pick means quality reproduction and efficient press performance.

IP Web® Gloss is a higher brightness, coated groundwood offset paper. Its good ink hold-out, level surface and internal strength assure runnability and trouble-free pressruns. IP Web has all the paper traits for quality printing for faithful 4-color process with crisp type and line reproductions.

ADDITIONAL IP PAPERS AND BOARDS

Free Sheet Converting and Specialty Grades

Springhill® Envelope
Gator-Hide® Envelope
Springhill® Tablet
Register Bond
Carbonizing Tissue
Converter Index
Adding Machine Paper
Placemat
Wall Board Tape
Manila File Folder
Kraft File Folder
Tabulating Index
Clay Coated Specialties
Resin Coated Specialties
Polyethylene Coated Specialties
Plastic Coated Specialties
Bleached Board Specialties

® Registered trademark of International Paper Company.
™ Trademark of International Paper Company.

Papers used in the Pocket Pal: *Cover,* Feedcote®, 10-pt. *Text,* Bookmark®, Blue-White, 60 lb.